CW00556944

A SHIP, A DREAM

AND

LAWRENCE OF ARABIA

A TRIUMPH BELATED

An autobiographical narrative

Edward Spurr

Published 2020

Graft Poetry
Frizingley Hall
Frizinghall Road
Bradford BD9 4LD
UK
graftpoetry.co.uk

Printed by Inprint + Design, University of Bradford

All rights reserved
© Edward John Lawrence Spurr

ISBN 978-1-9998878-4-1

Cover painting – W K Bicknell

Why has a poetry publisher brought out this book? Because I was asked and because I thought it was a brilliant story that needed to be published and which deserved a wide readership.

Jim Greenhalf and I have edited this publication between us.

– Nicholas Bielby, Editor, Graft Poetry

Editorial Note

Bradford's forgotten inventor and engineer Edward Spurr was born in 1907 and died in California in 1998 after an extraordinary lifetime during which he worked with Lawrence of Arabia on two types of high-performance speed boat, patented the elliptical wing used later on the Spitfire, contributed to the technologies that delivered Barnes Wallis' bouncing bomb on German dams in World War II and Frank Whittle's jet engine. Towards the end of his life this unassuming man wrote in longhand a memoir which he described as an autobiographical narrative. *A Ship, A Dream and Lawrence of Arabia* was edited by his son John Spurr and sub-titled *A Triumph Belated*. The remarkable thing in this story is that T E Lawrence – Aircraftman Shaw, as he then chose to be known – displayed a brilliant talent in sparking off Edward Spurr's creative engineering ability in the design of a completely new concept of high-speed boat with a fast guerrilla-like capability at sea – hopefully for Britain's Royal Navy – employing tactics he adapted from the deserts of Arabia during World War I.

Like his father Edward, John Spurr, who edited his father's story, is a design engineer who worked for many years in California's Silicon Valley, with breaks to work for Lotus Cars, Ricardo & Co at Shoreham-by-Sea, and BMC in Australia. He and his artist wife Alice live beside Tagish Lake in the Yukon Territory wilderness of Canada, an hour's boat-ride (35km) from the nearest road. In 1980, they went into the forests alone to build their log cabin home and gardens. They are surrounded by huge lakes, untouched mountains, forest wilderness and wildlife – bears, wolves, caribou, wildcats, eagles. A true (though regularly frozen) paradise.

John's mother Ruth Edwina Spurr (*née* Goodman) grew up in Shoreham-by-Sea, Sussex. She met Edward Spurr at the Bell Inn, Cowes, Isle of Wight, which was owned and operated by her mother. They were married on 11 May 1935.

– *Jim Greenhalf and Nicholas Bielby*

3

I dedicate this book to distressed Mother Nature

and to the domesticated pets and wild life of land, sea and air which she so diligently and so tenaciously evolved, and which often are so cruelly ill-treated, and so often, so wantonly and so heartlessly slaughtered by wayward human beings.

— Edward Spurr

Contents

Foreword *by John Spurr*

This story has been rather long in the telling for a number of reasons. My father never, really, got over the failure of his efforts to get the work that he and T E Lawrence[1] jointly developed accepted by the British Admiralty or Government. It was a matter of disbelief that they could have been so blind to the potential benefits of the research and development that was so clearly pregnant with promise. He met with such a lack of official interest at the time when he was promoting it, that the idea of later writing about it never interested him. He thought it was, indeed, dead, buried and best forgotten.

He then, when living in the USA, saw the article written by H F King, MBE, *Another Lawrence, "Aircraftman Shaw" and Air Cushion Craft*, which appeared in the *Flight International* Supplement, 24 February 1966. This rekindled his interest. Although Mr. King's article was mostly excellent, it did not, and could not, really tell the full story. Only my father and Lawrence knew that. Also, as is made clear in the book, it was Lawrence who advised my father at the beginning of their friendship that it would be wise to tell no one of his research as, at that stage, it would serve no useful purpose. And another deterrent to publicising the work, back in the mid-1930s, was its potential value in relationship to national defence.

As retirement settled in, he began to write a full autobiography, as something to do, and of course, the episodes with Lawrence took centre stage. Fifteen years before Lawrence – then T E Shaw in the RAF – met my father in 1933 at a boatyard in Hythe near Southampton, his reputation, as a hero of the desert campaign against the Ottoman Empire in the Great War, drove this quiet man of action to seek anonymity under an assumed name. Shaw's passion for fast-moving boats was the connection that started the occasional working relationship with my father. As he makes clear throughout his memoir, my father deeply admired Shaw, both as a human being and as an engineer.

---

[1] When my father met T.E. Lawrence he had changed his name to T.E. Shaw, and it was as T.E. Shaw that my father always knew him.

His original manuscript was far too long if he just wanted to concentrate on the story of Lawrence's genius and its impact on high-speed boat design with an emphasis on naval military applications. The subsequent editing of the manuscript took years to complete as he was literally in no hurry. It was not quite completed when he died on 5 February 1998 at the age of 90. He suffered a major stroke and went almost immediately. He was most fortunate to have been fully active and independent to the end.

Although it was clear he wanted me to finish off the story and book, I too, was in no great hurry; I was heavily involved with my own interests. I dearly wanted to get to it, but I had to procrastinate. So, we made a fine pair.

At first it was difficult to accept leaving out so much of the original manuscript as I found it so humorous, generally interesting and enjoyable, but in the interests of confining the story to the topic at hand, it was the correct choice.

John Spurr with Misty

I must make clear that none of the words in the story are mine. I have played a minor role in editing some chapters, and that

7

amounted to no more than choosing what I thought should be retained from the manuscript. In 2007 the Bradford *Telegraph & Argus* newspaper published what it called a mini-series of articles about my father's life, based on his unpublished manuscript. Later, I was helped by the journalist who had written and compiled those articles, Jim Greenhalf, who in turn introduced me to Nicholas Bielby, the publisher of this book. Like my father, I was fortunate in that respect. His passage through life was also assisted by numerous friends and acquaintances.

I was lucky to have had such a father. He never forced anything on me, and always fully supported whatever I did. When I was a young man we worked marvellously together and I loved designing with him, it was such fun. I was most fortunate to serve a designer's apprenticeship with him.

He was a kind and gentle man at heart, with a deep sense of humour.

Edward John Lawrence Spurr　　　　　　　　　*18 August 2019*
Tagish Lake, Yukon, Territory, Canada

Introduction *by Edward Spurr*

This is a simple story, and it is simply told: A young engineer met a remarkable man. This man captivated the engineer, who became the instrument for the sculpting of the other's dream. The dream was of a ship, and the ship was a fast one; the dream was of a navy, and it was a British navy.

It happened a long time ago, and all for the love of *This blessed plot, this earth, this realm, this England.*

Pitifully, the effort was wasted, and, woefully, soon forgotten.

*

It is my hope that history will, in addition to recording T.E. Lawrence's earlier exploits, record T.E. Shaw's great love of the sea and what he did so many years ago to foster the development of safe, comfortable, high speed travel on it.

Words are rarely adequate and, however well-chosen, they cannot fully express thoughts and feelings, but I have done what I can with those that I know. As we all do, for as yet we have no other choice, Shaw lived and died, and one day those who knew him will also die. Then, words only will remain and posterity, as always, must be satisfied by them.

It is the pen gives immortality to men, as Master Wace told us over eight hundred years ago. This being so, perhaps this late pen will add yet a fraction more to the width of the already wide track trodden by T.E. Lawrence toward everlasting fame. Should it do so, then I would be well-satisfied.

This narrative will represent my *à compte III* to L. of A., and as I grow no younger, my final one.

God rest his daring and curious soul!

*

By the year 1933 the V-bottom high speed planing boat had been developed to a reasonably high degree of performance in terms

Edward Spurr, aged 80

of its speed on water and its cost to build. Development work on this kind of boat, better known as the speedboat or, technically, as the hard chine displacement boat, had begun long before the First War and had continued, sometimes steadily, sometimes intermittently, up to that year. The creditable results achieved were got mainly by using cut-and-try methods, and what scientific knowledge had by that time been recorded was scant and elementary.

The knowledge gained by the boat-builder in his yard, and the naval architect on his drawing board, was held as a trade or professional secret to be brought out, when needed, autocratically and without close explanation. The design backdrop was one of black magic, expertly divined and administered by connoisseurs. All this was considered perfectly normal procedure, and accepted without question by all concerned.

There is, however, more to the design of an all-round, high-performance boat than sheer speed and first cost, and it was unfortunate that many of the other desired qualities still needed to improve the V-bottom were, if not entirely lacking, then seriously lagging when compared with the design immemorial of the Admiralty pattern or round-bottom boat. (For the benefit of the layman, it is mentioned that the V-bottom boat skims or planes over the surface of the water, whereas the round-bottom boat ploughs its way through it.)

The round-bottom boat had been built in all shapes and sizes for thousands of years, and its qualities, good and not-so-good, could be discussed, theoretically and practically, with almost strict accuracy. This was not so at that time in matters relating to the planing boat. There still remained much to be learned before guesswork and rule-of-thumb methods could be eliminated. There was a strong need for creative thought, backed by sound mathematical theory, and for a determined model test programme, aerodynamic as well as hydrodynamic.

Two of the desired qualities that rated poorly in the planing boat as compared with the round bottom boat, were its hard and uncomfortable ride and its inadequate load carrying ability. These were grave faults, which would have to be improved if these boats were ever to become more than special purpose craft of limited scope.

This, then, was about where matters stood when I first met Aircraftman Shaw, at Hythe, in Hampshire, in the summer of 1933.

Shaw had worked closely on these boats over the previous four years, and had been in an influential position, midway between builder and user, for most of that time. He had gained a first-hand, practical experience of the planing boat at sea and in the workshops, and many of the design improvements he had suggested during those years had been eagerly accepted and promptly applied. Further, he had played a leading and determined part in obtaining official acceptance of the planing boat for all naval services in the RAF.

I, on the other hand, was an outsider; an interloper "of the very first water, undiluted". I was a mechanical engineer from the automobile industry and, at that time, hardly knew one end of a boat from the other.

As it turned out, my ignorance was to be an advantage.

*

Late on a dull September afternoon in 1938, a strange, sleek, racing craft sped all but airborne over the surface of Lake Windermere, on the border of Lancashire and Westmoreland, in the North of England.

Strapped to the seat in the narrow, streamlined cockpit of the speeding craft was an unknown, untried young man who carried in his heart a single fervent wish to keep a solemn promise to a friend some time dead. With that roaring, straight-waked sprint over Lake Windermere, the wish was granted, and the promise kept.

The story of the preparation and the struggle behind that event began more than thirty years earlier at Fagley, in Yorkshire, in a little back-to-back cottage, the home of a Bradford postman.

Perhaps, from the beginning, the early preparation, the later struggle, and that roaring sprint over Lake Windermere were fore-ordained, and the young man given no other choices.

Chapter 1: Early Springtime and the Beginning of the Road

I read my first book on aerodynamics during the First War while still at elementary school in Bradford. I was ten and I found the book in our class library at the Wellington Road Elementary School – a short, single row of books in a glass-fronted cupboard. The key to this cupboard was jealously guarded by our teacher, the – to me – elderly Miss Roberts. I cannot now imagine how on earth that book on aerodynamics got into our tiny library. I read it from cover to cover and was fascinated by all it told me. I kept on re-reading it. I well remember the early aerofoil profiles shown in its illustrations and the forms of airflow patterns depicted around them at all angles of attack. The explanations of lift, drag, and thrust, I quickly grasped and never forgot. I learnt a lot about the behaviour of air in motion when I read that simple textbook.

My father used to say that I was born with a pencil as well as a cricket bat in my hand. This modest talent of mine of being able to draw things, particularly mechanical things, kept me quiet as a mouse when indoors; and this extra gift must have been a heaven-sent relief to my parents. Quite by chance, by the age of twelve, I had taught myself to draw as an engineer draws. This bonus to my already well-demonstrated artistic ability cost me no intellectual strain of any kind. Gradually and unfortunately, over the years, as I began to use instruments more and more, I lost my early free-style deftness and this loss, when I stopped to think about it, saddened me.

My thirteenth year was an important one. It forecast my life pattern clearly; although I didn't see it clearly at the time and neither did anyone else, which surprises me now.

Opposite our home in Ashgrove was a good-sized orchard owned by a schoolmistress. Eric Bentley, Willie Atkinson, Dick East and I used to steal apples from this orchard during the long summer holidays; they were "cookers", but that did not stop us. The orchard had a five-foot high, wooden-paling fence around it and the paling slats were of triangular cross section. Each side of the cross section was about one-and-a-quarter inches wide. This triangular cross section gave me an idea.

13

One wet and miserable day, the kind of day Bradford has many of in wintertime, from a spot in the fence not easily noticed, I removed one of the palings. The fence was in bad repair anyway; I merely helped it on a bit. I cut two pieces from the paling, each about ten inches long. With both ends of these made pointed and spaced in parallel, about six inches apart, I nailed a five-inch long platform across the top. I cut the platform from the end of an orange box, a popular material with me at the time because the price was right. In the centre of this platform I burnt a hole with the tapered end of our poker (at home we had a coal fire burning all the time) and then drove into it a piece of rough "dowel" rod cut from a child's Union Jack stick. The stick acted as a mast and across it I fixed a square, paper sail.

This was my first-ever working model of a boat: it was a catamaran. I had never seen or heard of a catamaran, so as far as I was concerned, it was an invention. It just seemed to me that the twin-hull design was the best way to obtain a stable boat. After more than sixty years' reflection I still think it was the cleverest and most intelligent innovation I ever thought of. As soon as the boat was completed, I floated it on the nearest rain pond – there were plenty of them in and around Ashgrove on wet days. I was highly delighted with my performance and overwhelmed by my own genius.

One of my friends who saw the experiment was Harry Creek. Harry was my age and the middle brother of the three Creek brothers, the others being Willie and Jack. Willie, the oldest, was a dedicated boy scout and a born leader. Young Jack turned out to be a brilliant scholar and very intellectual. One day Jack, as a little boy, was teaching me how to knot a *timber hitch* when he stopped, looked up at me and said, "Lines are said to be parallel when they lie upon the same plane, and, when produced either way, do not meet". I asked him why he had told me that. He said, "I am fond of Euclid, and I want to share him with you." Harry, on the other hand, was normal and bred rabbits. He told me that it wasn't difficult to get them to breed, but that it taxed his patience to get them to sit up in line and beg for rum and butterballs.

After the launching and the successful trials of my new boat, Harry, in spite of his down to earth character, was overcome by my

14

emotion and his own admiration for my work as a naval architect. This swayed him to pay me the generous compliment of recording my brilliant achievement in verse. In my grown-up wisdom I now recognize his tribute as having the smack of a more gentle clerihew. I'll bet he knew it all the time but didn't want to show off. He wrote it instead of doing his German homework and it ran:

> Eddie Spurr
> Built *Hotspur*,
> A smashing, dashing, two-hulled yacht
> That kept straight up, no matter what!

The next day at school, Harry was unable to recite one word of *Die Lorelei*, except the title, and he was given fifty lines by our German mistress *Ma Crudder* (Miss Crowther) for gross neglect of his studies. This was a bitter lesson to him and, the glamour gone, he said he would never write verse again.

In this same year, using our kitchen table as a drawing board, I drew my favourite tramcar on a piece of cartridge paper. This paper I had bought out of the few coppers I called my capital. It was tramcar No. 240, on the Undercliffe route, a double-decker and, except for the front and rear extremities of the upper deck, fully enclosed. Resplendent on its gold-edged, navy-blue, lower side panels, the No. 240 proudly carried the City of Bradford's coat of arms. It was a beautiful and well-proportioned tramcar. I drew it in side view, in India ink, exactly as an engineer would draw it, for this was, to me, the clearest and most sensible way to describe it for posterity. This drawing was appropriated from my personal independent file by my manual instructor Mr. Ellis, at Hanson, when in a moment of altruistic zeal I displayed it to him. Seventeen years afterward, at the invitation of my old English master Willie Cox, I revisited Hanson in the guise of a distinguished old boy, it was shown to me by my old instructor.

Frank Hartley first drew my attention to the beauty of the tramcar. Frank was my age and, like me, was the son of a Bradford postman. His favourite tramcar was No. 38, also on the Undercliffe route. He built a model of No. 38 and I started to build my No. 240.

15

When I was halfway through, Frank took it from me, but whether he ever completed it, I don't know. Frank won a scholarship and elected to attend the Bradford School of Art instead of Hanson, so we gradually lost touch with each other. In later life he became a recognized authority on the history and design of the tramcar; I remember he had at least one of his models accepted by the Science Museum, at Kensington.

I became fascinated with a set of diagrams I saw of a side valve, four stroke, internal combustion engine. It showed all the four strokes of the cycle, each with the piston and poppet valves correctly phased. I went to sleep that night repeating to myself, INDUCTION, COMPRESSION, FIRING, EXHAUST and with a never-to-be-forgotten appreciation of the potency of well executed and clearly annotated diagrams.

Laurence Metcalfe, a close friend from elementary school days, was the son of the chief engineer at Wilson's, a local spinning mill. Many a Saturday morning would find Laurie and me in and out of the repair shops at the mill or, sometimes, swimming in the open water tank, high and cold, on the workshop roof. As a special treat, Mr. Metcalfe would take us into the engine room to see the big, single cylinder double-acting, horizontal steam engine, which was the main power source for all floors of the mill. It seemed a huge power plant to us; the massive flywheel was so large in diameter that the engine room ceiling was, by design, cut away for its clearance. From this colossal, slow-running flywheel were driven perhaps six or eight white cotton rope belts, which delivered their power to the line shafting on the floors above.

This beautifully built, spic and span, power plant, by Cole, Marchant and Morley of Bradford, gave me my first real feeling of engineering ecstasy and brought James Watt and George Stephenson into the rest of my life. It remains one of the most satisfying engineering sights I have ever seen. I can still smell the warm, oily atmosphere that prevailed in the engine room at Wilson's. The spotlessly clean, black and white, squared-tiled floor, and my recollected feel of the warm, highly polished, steel guard rails, remain pleasant memories.

Edward Spurr at home in Fagley

Fred Metcalfe was an engineer of the George Stephenson school. He had been brought up in steam. He was a practical, all-round engineer. Mechanically and electrically, nothing fazed him, and he could use any tool or machine with skill. I owe him a lot, not only for what he taught me, but also for the inspiration he gave me when I was but a youngster. He, truly, introduced me to engineering as a life-work.

During the First War, in whatever spare time he could command, Fred Metcalfe designed and built a small, open, two-seater motorcar. Over three years I saw this car grow from an idea on paper to a real thing of great mechanical beauty. It had a second-hand, vertical, two cylinders, water-cooled engine, with a disc-type,

17

variable speed transmission, and a leather V-belt final drive to the solid rear axle. The body had ash frames and ribs and a plywood skin which was enamelled green. Mr. Metcalfe put the letters LM (young Laurence's initials), made from thin brass sheet and highly polished, on the front of the radiator, and called it the *LM CYCLE CAR*.

On the car's first run, after all that work, the back axle bent and Mr. Metcalfe quietly sold the car for scrap. Its sad end gave me a violent stomach ache.

The whole process of designing and building a vehicle, however, sank deeply into my uncluttered mind. It was a great instruction and I never forgot it. I owe much to Fred Metcalfe and to Wilson's mill on Moorside Road.

With the changes made in the woollen industry at Bradford after the Second War (owing to the closing of many local textile mills and the modernizing of others) Wilson's spinning mill – properly known as Moorside Mills – became, in 1974, the Bradford Industrial Museum. The museum preserves the genuine mill atmosphere; and the machines, I am told, are almost all in working order. There is a Transport Gallery; and it delights me to know that among the exhibits are several Jowett cars. I hope that the Scott *Squirrel* motorcycle, the Scott *Sociable* three-wheeler cycle car and the P and M *Panther* motorcycle are also on display for posterity to see. All these machines played an important part in Bradford and District's automobile manufacturing history over fifty years.

Fred Metcalfe would be as proud as I am to know that the old mill is still carrying its head high.

Over the road from our house, next to the warehouse, was a single-storey, redbrick building in poor state of repair. It had two rooms and earthen floors. When I was thirteen, three men rented it from Sam Dalby. They turned it into a small engineering business, naming it the Ashgrove Engineering Company. I painted their outside sign for them. They clubbed together and paid me three shillings for my trouble.

I helped them when they were installing their machine tools and workbenches. I remember a six-inch centre lathe, a radial drill, a drill press, a small planer, a horizontal miller, a vertical miller and a small toolmaker's lathe. All these machines were bedded down on the hard, earthen floor. The machines were already well-used; but I was very impressed when I saw what they could do.

Soon I was running errands for the men and delivering some of their smaller precision pieces. I got oranges, apples, mintoes, chocolate and once, a silver shilling, for doing these chores. Sometimes one of them would stand by my side and let me operate the handles on the centre lathe.

After a year or so in business, the fellows at Ashgrove Engineering Company put up a wood and corrugated iron, high-roofed shed, for use as a non-ferrous foundry. The youngest one, little more than an apprentice, told me that they had financed the new extension on their losses. I could never figure out how such a thing could be done. Where did the money come from when you were working at a loss?

Once in operation, the foundry became my main interest in life. I learned to skim for the partners on "pouring" day. While two of them poured from the hand-held, T-bar-cradled, ceramic crucible, I skimmed away the surface dross with a piece of steel rod, shaped at the skimming end like a walking stick handle. They taught me to make multiple sand-moulds for small brass components such as hinge plates, water closet door handles, toilet cistern parts, and pipe fittings. All three partners were very nice to me and swore only under their breath, when I pretended not to hear.

Being smaller than any of them, I was permitted to clean out the coke-fired pits. There were three of these furnace pits, all in a single line; each one was about two-and-a-half feet square, and four feet deep to its loose fire bars. I could lift out these bars, one at a time, and get down to the draught floor without difficulty. At the top, each of the three pits led into a horizontal flue, covered by loose, steel, top plates. This flue led directly to the bottom of the vertical chimney. This chimney was fabricated from sheet metal and was about fifteen inches in diameter and twenty-five feet high. The draught it created was unbelievable. Though my job was cold as well as grimy, I never complained or questioned my privilege. It was an honour for me to be accepted into their fraternity.

At thirteen I became a foundryman and all that I learned, and it was a lot, stood me in good stead for the next fifty years; especially so when I had to design some of the most complicated cylinder blocks the automobile industry has ever seen... many, many of them.

School homework was the heavy cross I bore one way and another for thirteen depressing years. I regret the wasted time. In the early years, it had to be done for convention's sake, but it was done lightly and with as little effort and concentration as possible. At elementary school and at high school I chose my friends carefully so that, as a group, we owed nothing to books and everything to sport and the outdoors. This early astuteness paid high dividends, and we all put off for years the evil day, and the energy-wasting process, of achieving matriculation.

Our ideals slipped a little at times in our fight against a fancy, good-for-nothing education. On one occasion at high school I took second place in my form in physics and was promptly jeered by some of my classmates who, because of my past performances, could not believe that I could have put them behind me unaided. I was very depressed about this superb performance of mine. To this day I do not know what came over me. How was I to know, at that early age, that all that stuff about pulleys and ropes and weights and F equals ma and mirrors and tuning forks and thermometers and glass prisms came naturally to me? I was careful not to get caught in that net again. From that time forward I decided they could stuff their physics.

By the time my cronies and I reached Form *Va* we were fourteen years old and beginning to feel grown up. I played a leading role in producing our monthly, handwritten, class magazine. We called it *The Va Pie: In Which We All Have a Finger.* I drew mild caricatures, and wrote simple, class-orientated doggerel. I thought the magazine was superb, but not so our English master Willie Cox who, seeing it one day by unlucky chance, disapproved of it strongly. But he did ask me to draw caricatures for the Hanson magazine. I never did.

Chapter 2: The Welcome Call to the Drawing Board

While at Singer in 1932, I was surprised and excited to receive, out of the blue, a telegram from Raymond Mays of Bourne, Lincolnshire, asking me to discuss the possibility of my joining him and Peter Berthon on the design of a new British *grand prix* racing car. I embraced this opportunity with enthusiasm and rushed by train to Bourne as fast as I could. The terms of my engagement were soon settled and within two weeks I was back at Bourne, ready for work.

Murray Jamieson, then with Austin at Birmingham, was already moonlighting inside the small group at Bourne. Once a week or so he would pay us a flying visit in his Morris Minor for special discussions and to air his latest ideas on engine design. Jamieson was a supercharger expert and had earlier worked with Amherst Villiers, an old friend and helper of Mays, on similar work. I liked M.J. very much. We kept in touch until the time of his death by accident, at Brooklands track, only a few years later.

At Bourne I first worked with my drawing board installed in a garage at Mays' home, Eastgate House; but as summer turned into winter I was moved into the house itself to an upper, back bedroom. In this small room, with added financial support from Humphrey Cook, the White Riley and then the classic E.R.A. were born.

Buckle, our chief mechanic from Wolverhampton, was already established at Bourne. John Huggins, who had been at Triumph with me, in the motorcycle design office, joined the company, at my suggestion, as my assistant. John had served his time at Coventry Climax. He knew his job well and I found his help invaluable. We became close friends.

We were an able and serious team of enthusiasts. But we had our moments. Peter Berthon never failed to lighten our burdens with his special humour whenever the opportunity arose. I remember being in the throes of a design discussion with him when he lighted a cigarette, then, still in deep thought, flicked the burning match into a huge, open vat of petroleum. I watched spellbound, then petrified. Nothing happened. "That reminds me", he said, "It's time to fill the Primus stove for tea-up." We were all young, there were no personality problems. We all worked hard and liked it. Mays himself was a quiet man, but deeply enthusiastic and surprisingly tenacious.

His mother had arranged for me to make my digs at the local pub. I think it was called the *New Inn* and was almost directly opposite Eastgate House. It turned out to be a touch of genius on Mrs. Mays' part. The elderly and kindly landlady fed me as I have never been fed before or since. I was treated like a lord, fed like a fighting cock and I loved it. My bedroom was lit by candlelight. The "bog" was an old-fashioned, outside privy. That didn't worry me. I was used to that from my days in Ashgrove. Who, I thought, knowing digs as I did, could be overly concerned about a blue and frozen backside on a few winter's eves when every meal was a feast and the bed so clean and warm and comfortable? Not me! I have stayed in many fine hotels, in many countries, but none pleased me better than that little inn in Bourne. John Huggins joined me at the inn and later, when he married (I was his best man) he spent his honeymoon there. What better recommendation than that?

My first assignment at Bourne was the design of a six-cylinder, five litre, supercharged, double-overhead-camshaft racing engine. The work went well from the start but, halfway through the task, John and I were rushed off to Henry Meadows' at Wolverhampton, our uncompleted rolls of drawings tucked under our arms. Once there, we were to complete the general design of the engine and then, without the wasting of a single second, make and issue the detail drawings for the manufacture of three of these engines at the Meadows' factory. The engines were to be built and tested in double-quick time, in readiness for competition in the 1934 season. In engineering parlance, it was a *tear-arse* job. But it was exciting and neither John nor I belly-ached.

Our work at Wolverhampton had continued at a fast pace, on the drawing board and in the workshops. Many of the more important components had been finished and checked for accuracy and they all looked good. Then, suddenly, we were told to stop all we were doing and to return post-haste to Bourne. We found the five-litre engine project had been cancelled. If I remember correctly, this was because the international five-litre racing class was to be discontinued. Immediately we began a new project, the brainchild of Raymond Mays and Peter Berthon. In essence, we were to take a Riley sports car engine and chassis and modify it for road racing. Accordingly, in that back bedroom at Eastgate House, John Huggins, Peter Berthon and myself frantically made quick drafts of the one-and-a-half litre, six-cylinder Riley engine showing a new cylinder head, valve gear, crankshaft and a front-mounted Roots-type supercharger.

When completed, this highly developed Riley engine made history in the hands of Raymond Mays at Brooklands and elsewhere. Installed in its racing chassis, the car became known as the White Riley, and it turned out to be a first-rate design study for the even more famous E.R.A. car which was to come along immediately afterward.

This was a hectic time for all of us and it became ritual for John and me to work until eleven or twelve o'clock at night; but this was no real hardship. We sensed that we were living an important part of British motor racing history.

Leaving Mays' home late one night in pitch dark, I walked into the trunk of a huge tree, oak or elm, in the garden at the side of the main driveway. I suffered agonizingly, but not in silence. John, to his credit, did not guffaw. Bruised, swollen, with a headache for days, I rued my negligence. Even today, when I think of Eastgate House, my next thought is of that blasted oak… or elm.

By me, as I write, I am looking at the first rough draft sketch I made for Peter Berthon of what was to become the new breed of cars from Bourne. I rediscovered it a few years ago, hidden underneath the tracing-cloth wrapper of my dear, old Donkin. As I look at this rough layout, on an old and faded piece of tracing paper, I feel that it all happened only yesterday. Even today, the design looks business-like and fully capable of the job it had to do to retrieve and uphold British prestige on road and track.

Late in my sojourn at Henry Meadows' I was approached by Hubert Scott-Paine with an offer to join him as his mechanical designer at the British Power Boat Company at Hythe, near Southampton. Meadows' were building power units for Scott-

Paine's boats and during one of Scott-Paine's infrequent visits to Wolverhampton, he put the offer to me. At first I demurred.

Scott-Paine was already busily engaged on the design and construction of a special racing boat, later to be known as *Miss Britain III*, in preparation for a challenge he had made to Gar Wood of America for the return of the British International Trophy (also known as the Harmsworth Trophy). This venture intrigued me greatly and played strongly on my always intense, patriotic sentiment. Finally, after some further elbowing by proxy (Scott-Paine was a very persistent man), and my keen interest and curiosity getting the better of me, I accepted his offer.

This decision was to lead me straight into the most exhilarating partnership I have ever known, one that was to change the direction and pattern of my life for many years ahead.

I joined Scott-Paine at his boat yard early in September 1933 (note that this date is very important). I found good digs near the high street at the start of the country lane that ran directly into Southampton some ten or twelve miles away. My new environment, at the edge of the New Forest, was like that of a nineteenth century hamlet, flanked by the sea. I liked it. Settling down in such tranquil surroundings was easy and without worrying job pressures.

My first bit of office space, shared with somebody else, was situated in the main rather small block of office buildings near the yard's front gate. But I needed more space, so almost immediately I cajoled the general manager at the yard, Mr. S.N. Barker, into letting me have a much better facility within the main assembly plant.

Here I was joined by young Les Still who, for a time, became my assistant. Les straight away filled me in on all the boat and boatyard terms I ought to know, for which kindness, being a landlubber, I was grateful. The days were pleasant and the work unhurried; my digs were excellent. In the idyllic surroundings in which I found myself, I felt like a Rockefeller running his empire from a penthouse pad, high on a paradisiacal Puerto Rican beach.

At last I had escaped the grim, life-sapping existence found in so many of the engineering workshops and drawing offices of my time. Often a design office was looked upon as a "damned nuisance" and put in some dark corner of the factory, with artificial lighting,

Three views of the British Power Boat yard in the 1930s, by kind permission of Waterside Heritage, centre@watersideheritage.org.uk

rank air and few amenities. Hythe was different. For the first time in my life I could sit and ponder in pleasant surroundings without having to gauge my performance against a ticking clock on a distant wall. I revelled in my freedom. I had been lifted from what seemed to be a dark, miserable confinement and placed in warm, comforting sunshine, under a bright blue sky. I had been put among friends who were untouched by the hardships that still lingered on from the tail end of the industrial revolution. My fondness for Hythe grew. The countryside and seascapes spoiled me; never again was I to be a contented "inlander". I had one fear, a feeling that it couldn't last and that, too soon, the gypsy in me would resent my contentment.

One afternoon during the first days in my mid-factory office where, through its wide expanse of window, we could look down and view the whole of the assembly bay and more, Les Still called my attention to a man in grey slacks, sports jacket and woollen sweater, who was making his way across the main floor. Les said, "Do you know who that is?" I hadn't the faintest idea who it could be and said so. He said, "That's Lawrence of Arabia". I looked at Les unbelievingly, but he was quite serious. He went on to say that Lawrence, known at the yard as Mr. Shaw, or more officially as Aircraftman Shaw, spent much of his time with us and worked as a test pilot and liaison officer between the Royal Air Force and the British Power Boat Company.

As I looked at the man I was genuinely and completely awestruck. It was as though I had been asked to view Julius Caesar or William the Conqueror at close hand.

In my early teens, I had read a lot of reports in Sunday newspapers about this mysterious and legendary figure and his heroic deeds in the deserts of Arabia. The newspapers always called him the *Uncrowned King of Arabia.* Like others, I came to think of him as a man of mystery and intrigue and as a kingmaker to boot. A romantic aura surrounded him that made me think of the Drury Lane Theatre and *Desert Song*, Rudolph Valentino and *The Sheik.* When I was about twenty-three, soon after I had read the best parts of my library's copy of *Revolt in the Desert,* I had pictured him as a courageous and granite-faced Norseman, a born and ruthless killer.

Now, after setting eyes on him, I began to wonder what kind of man he was really.

That evening after dinner I began to think again about the afternoon's incident. I reminded myself that Shaw had looked, at a guess, about five-foot-six in height (not a bad guess, as it turned out) and that he was blue-eyed and fair-haired. He had looked fresh-air fit and ruggedly good looking. The latter because of his strong, chiselled features and resolute chin. His expression was that of a quiet, reserved man. I got the feeling he missed nothing that was going on around him, not in the way of a busy martinet, but with the calmness of Rodin's *Thinker*. I decided in my reverie that I liked the look of him.

My first chance to try my hand at piloting a speedboat came unexpectedly, through the kindness and thoughtfulness of a young fellow named Boyle who was, among many other things, a test pilot at Power Boat. One morning, at his suggestion, he took me out on the Solent in Scott-Paine's own craft *Black Panther,* a sleek, hard chine, 32-footer with a 100 h.p. Meadows engine. Out on the open water Boyle expertly demonstrated to me the art of handling the craft.

I was captivated and my enthusiasm for high speed boats, especially their design, began immediately. I asked a lot of questions, which Boyle answered patiently and very clearly. I took in all that he told me, my concentration never flagged. I could not have wished for a better teacher or a more painless breaking-in. Finally, for a short time, Boyle allowed me to take over the wheel and I got my first practical lesson at the helm of a very fast boat – for those days.

The craft skimmed along beautifully. To feel the wheel in my own hands and the powerful thrust in my back was a delight. The sharp V-bow sliced open the choppy sea surface like a scalpel in the hands of a quick eyed, sure fingered, master surgeon. There was nothing capricious about the behaviour of *Black Panther*. She did what she was told and she did it promptly. Soon confident, I was able to manoeuvre her with ease. Buoys and slower moving craft were passed and cleared with such smooth, banked sweeps that I was later reminded of John Cobb in his *Railton Special,* on the rim of the Byfleet banking at Brooklands. It was a first-class and, at the same time, a memorable lesson which I got from Boyle. By chance and colossal cheek I was soon to make use of it.

Neither Boyle nor I knew just what he had started that sunny morning, early in September 1933, out on the open Solent. Boyle was the one that started all that was to follow. Yet even today, modest young man that he was, I doubt that he would believe me if I tried to explain the tremendous influence he cast over me and the enthusiasm and determination he engendered in me to pursue, for the greater part of my life, the research, design and development of a new line of high speed, ocean-going ships of large displacement. He prepared, by a few days, my inevitable path toward Aircraftman Shaw, who, in his genius, was to show me the exact direction I was to take and the goal I was to capture. Boyle's brief interlude in my life provided another firm push toward my unavoidable destiny; perhaps, even then, deep down, I knew it.

Overnight I began to take a keen interest in the design of high speed hulls. Without delay I read all I could find on the subject: new and old yachting and motor boat magazines, both popular and trade; textbooks from the library; and the *Encyclopaedia Britannica*. What I found was meagre enough; but it was a beginning and I began to learn something of the planing boat's general naval architecture and applied hydrodynamics. I pressed on. Painstakingly, from a popular first year text-book (I forget its title and author) loaned to me by Les Still, I systematically and tenaciously studied naval architecture and marine engineering as taught at engineering college. This, in a simple way, gave me knowledge of and background in traditional ship design.

I worked long hours at my new task and within weeks began to develop ideas of my own for what I thought would be improvements in the design of high speed hulls. The ideas were disconnected and, as I soon began to realize, technically immature. But I was keen to prove my ideas. I felt strongly that I should try them out quickly and practically. However, the more I worked at my ideas and problems the more the early excitement and keenness to do something quickly and concretely faded. I slowly and surely came to acknowledge the enormity of the task I had set myself.

It was then that I decided to forget the ticking clock and, from that moment, to study diligently and lengthily the basic hydrodynamics and special aerodynamics of the speed-boat rather than its general layout and usual kind of construction. I felt that if I could stick firmly to this plan I would see in which direction pure theory would lead me. Then, perhaps, I should be lucky enough to stumble on a classical breakthrough of some kind. I could see it was going to be a long job; but I knew I would enjoy it.

I made a list of the separate investigations I intended to make. It was not as long as I expected, but I had a feeling it would grow as time went on. I was sure each item would break down into a number of subdivisions.

I had been right; the list did grow longer and, as my knowledge widened, it became more and more detailed in purpose. I never panicked at the size and scope of my programme perhaps because, in my abysmal ignorance, I truly believed that my enthusiasm and determination would nourish my creative talents.

At the beginning of these investigations I suffered confusion in deciding which item on my list I should tackle first. To get off on the right foot seemed important to avoid back-tracking later. The early work, I thought, must form a solid foundation for all that was to follow. For a day or two I hesitated.

Then, one morning, I awoke full of pep and with the conviction that I should begin my enquiries with the planing surface itself.

I started at the bottom in my investigations, the boat's bottom; and this early work led naturally and progressively to all the later investigations and developments from the bottom up. Without this early work on the planing surface, all further enquiries would have been baulked by fantasy.

This initial determination of mine to further the design and development of the planing surface thrust me into the heart-breaking pursuit of a supership, a supership that was already being dreamed of in another's mind, a mind far greater than my own. This associate mind was to force its imprint on my own to such an extent that, for the first time in my life, I was able, without undue distress, to discipline and concentrate my own modest talents toward a purpose which, I soon began to recognize, was of major national importance.

The British Power Boat Company, 1941. This painting, by Bradford-born War Artist, Richard Eurich RA, shows the general layout – and the busyness – of the yard. The 'whale-back' Motor Gun Boats depicted here are larger, later developments from the boats Shaw worked on.

Image with kind permission of The National Maritime Museum, on whose website a larger, colour version of the picture (BHC1570) may be viewed.

Chapter 3: I Meet Aircraftman Shaw and Like Him

I first met and talked to Aircraftman Shaw in late September 1933. I was twenty-six years of age, and he was forty-five. The meeting was brief, formal and unexpected.

He had climbed the steep wooden steps to my office, high against the inside wall of the main assembly shed and stood quietly behind me while I turned from my drawing board and raised my head. I was surprised. Although I had grown accustomed to seeing him around the yard, I still felt a little awestruck to see him looking directly into my eyes. Without any fuss or introduction, he handed me a damaged connecting rod, taken from one of our smaller marine engines and asked me if I thought it was strong enough for its job.

He said nothing while I looked at and studied it (without fouling the fracture itself). It was of the split-small-end kind, with a pinch bolt for clenching it to the gudgeon pin. I pointed out to him that this kind of part was cluttered with stress risers (those critical portions of the rod section where the change of stress was sudden). Again, he said nothing while I made a few quick assumptions, fiddled with my slide rule and jotted the resulting figures on my pad. This took a little while. I told him the rod was theoretically strong enough as it was, but the design was not good and further trouble could be expected on other rods. I said that once in a while a badly-machined rod of that design would be likely to fail.

My answer seemed to please him, as though he had already written a similar opinion in his report. Taking the connecting rod from me, he quietly thanked me for my help, and then left. He walked down the wooden steps to the main floor below and then across the bay. I saw him pass through the huge sliding doors at the far end, into the sunlit yard beyond. When he reached the main slipway, he veered to the right and disappeared from my view.

It was a lovely summer day. I clearly recollect the bright colours of the sea, sky and the dazzling, white-painted sheds and jetty posts. Scotty had a passion for painting almost everything white, including the machines in the machine shop. About this white-paint idiosyncrasy of Scotty's, Wilf Pickerill, our machine

31

shop foreman and a close friend of mine, used to say that if we were to keep on painting the machines as we did, then our No.2 Herbert capstans would soon become No.4's.

After our first meeting, Shaw and I were on nodding terms. At this stage of our relationship, whenever he passed me in the yard he rarely spoke, although on one occasion he half stopped in his walk to say, "How many stress risers have you found today?" I would smile, give the slightest of nods and walk on. I had a built-in dread of appearing to force myself upon his attention. At the same time, I could not help thinking what a nice chap he would be to know.

After a short time, I began to overlook his awesome image, although I still kept my distance out of natural shyness and a genuine desire not to push myself unasked into his privacy.

In and around the yard Shaw was always active in some way: fetching and carrying; stooping and reaching; putting on his oil-skins for a trip to sea; making his way to the general supply store or the tool store; and, often, diligently writing in his handy pocket book.

I rarely saw him talking to others, especially as one of a group. He would go out of his way to avoid even an important one. Often, when he had a cluster of visiting V.I.P.'s from the Air Ministry or the R.A.F., Shaw would purposely hang around the tail end of the meandering bunch, trying his best to look as insignificant as possible. I would catch sight of him chatting to Ft. Lt. Beauforte-Greenwood, who was head of the Marine Equipment Branch of the Air Ministry or Ft. Lt. Norrington, his assistant. Shaw didn't seem to mind spending time with these officers. I used to nod to them myself, but that was all. Although I was in charge of mechanical design at the company, I was really quite small fry in terms of company visibility. I was a slow talker and no pusher. Our lives revolved around Scotty and S.N. Barker and they, quite rightly, took centre stage most of the time.

There was a story told about His Royal Highness the Prince of Wales and Shaw, which could have been true though, for obvious reasons, I strongly doubt it (one, of course, being the always impeccably practised ceremonial code of the Royal Family). I cannot recollect, perhaps I never knew, the finer details of the alleged incident.

T E Shaw with his beloved Brough Superior

The story went something like this: A large group of locally distinguished people were awaiting the arrival by flying boat at Southampton of the Prince of Wales. They were to welcome him to an important civic ceremony. A long, red carpet led from the top of the quayside steps to the expectant group awaiting his arrival. The flying boat landed on time and a 40-foot express cruiser carried the Prince toward the quay and the waiting dignitaries. Alighting at the quay, Edward, Prince of Wales, dashed up the steps, two at a time, ran along the red carpet, straight through the VIPs and cordially wrung the hand of Aircraftman Shaw, A/c 2. His Royal Highness and Shaw appeared to be oblivious of the disowned and now muttering group behind them. The two walked away together, the Prince with his hand on Shaw's shoulder, talking closely and informally.

All this, if true, must afterward have amused Shaw. He was by nature outrageously mischievous. He took a young boy's delight in cocking a snook at the haughty and dignified. In my old age, and I could be wrong, I find something classical about this kind of humour.

Shaw was genuinely camera-shy. I heard many local stories in and around Hythe, which bear out this assertion. He bore an intense dislike of watchful press cameras and of shutter-happy snap-shooters. I suppose all these stories became embellished in the re-telling, but, to me, each had the ring of truth. Usually every camera story ended by claiming that Shaw, at the sound of a shutter click, would ask for the offending camera, remove its film and then expose it to the light. It was said that he never failed to pay for the film roll and that when he handed back the camera to the disappointed photographer, it was with his complements and apologies.

These camera stories, and others that I heard around the yard, affected me strongly enough to convince me that it might be a mistake to risk taking a picture of anything or any person within sight of Shaw. In any case, as I had no camera of my own at that time, my temptation was curbed. On the other hand, on at least two occasions, it would have been interesting and educational to have recorded for posterity Shaw's remarkable self-possession when under sharp duress. Once, he put his bare elbow on a stiff, wire brush that was resting, bristles uppermost, on a fitter's bench; and again, when in uniform, face beaming, he took the hand of a crying little boy and escorted him across a busy street to his mother. The mother thanked the nice airman, and the child kicked his shins.

34

In both these instances Shaw uttered not a word of damnation at the moment of crisis; his expression demonstrated to perfection his mastery of mind over body. The look on his face was one of beatific placidity. Deep in the eye only was there a hint that the devil's neck was being wrung.

My opportunity to become a pilot in my own right arose with the welcome home of Scott-Paine from America, following his valiant though unsuccessful attempt in *Miss Britain III* to regain the British International Trophy from Gar Wood, in *Miss America X*, on the Detroit River.

Scott-Paine's Miss Britain III, *a V-hulled planing speed boat. As the pictures show, compared with* Empire Day *(p.122), there is a considerable amount of wash and spray, which wastes energy. The engine is mounted aft with a drive shaft going well forward to a gear box from which a long tail shaft returns to the propeller at the stern. Half this tail shaft is in the water and is held straight by two support brackets, one near the propeller. This power train is expensive in terms of weight and drag.*

The company planned to intercept the Empress of Britain (Scotty aboard) as she sailed majestically up the Solent and surround her with a high speed, spray-making flotilla of speedboats all the way to her dock at Southampton.

The instruction I received from Boyle stood me in good stead on this day. When most of the other craft had already departed on their mission, I was left at the jetty with two other companions. We were in an open 14-ft dinghy, the engine ticking over in neutral, but no pilot. He had disappeared completely. We were forgotten. And it started to rain. Neither of my companions – one of them was Wilf Pickerill – knew anything about boats. So after waiting a little longer for our missing pilot, I suddenly decided to make myself pilot and skipper. I undid the bow line, took the wheel, put the craft into forward gear and accelerated away from the jetty without even glancing around. Everything went well for us. Although the ocean was choppy, the afternoon wet and windy and all three of us got soaked to the skin, the outing gave us a busy and exciting couple of hours.

On returning to Hythe, I was careful to pick an open spot at the jetty, well away from all other marine activity. The boat gave a minor bump against the jetty's rubbing strip, but that was all.

I had other good luck that day. During our outing in the Solent, I found myself bouncing along at the side of Sir Malcolm Campbell who also was piloting a dinghy, just like my own. It was one of ours, one that he had borrowed for the occasion. This happened before he built his first *Blue Bird* high-speed boat. He was at that time already considering doing so with the possibility, if it were successful in its preliminary trials, of making an attempt on the World Water Speed Record. We got to know each other rather well between the hard bounces. It became a friendship we kept up until the time of his death in 1949 – almost sixteen years later.

I remember Sir Malcolm's concern for the comfort of myself and my companions in our open dinghy. He himself was fitted out in yellow oilskins from head to foot, while we were in ordinary soft hats and thin, inexpensive, Marks and Spencer raincoats. After this wet and bouncy introduction, when he discovered I had worked with Raymond Mays, whom he knew well, we met many times over the years, usually at his Piccadilly office and kept up a steady correspondence. I liked Sir Malcolm. I helped him on a number of occasions on matters relating to high-speed racing-boat design. He introduced me in 1936 to Fred Cooper, who designed his first *Blue Bird* boat and I made available to Fred some of my own research. It was I who later drew Sir Malcolm's attention to Apel's work in America on the three-point-suspension hull. He eventually took up this design and applied it to the design and layout of his second *Blue Bird*, built by Vosper's.

After the Second War, when I had settled in South Africa, Sir Malcolm let me have some of his redundant *Blue Bird* components, which I needed for *Miss X*, the South African boat I built for Bobby Bothner, then a city councillor of Johannesburg. *Miss X* obtained the South African water speed record in 1948 on the Vaal River. The boat, a three-pointer, was constructed around a hull that Bobby had bought from (Sir) George Eyston, who had used it as a practice boat. At that time Eyston was showing a keen interest in the water speed record held by Sir Malcolm, a quest he later gave up.

I first met Captain George Eyston at Brooklands Track in October 1933. Scotty sent me there to talk to him about Diesel engines. The day after I met him he was to make an attempt on the world's fastest Diesel speed with an A.E.C. oil-engined car. We met again in 1938 when we were both elected Fellows of the Royal Society of St. George.

The Eyston hull I completely redesigned and rebuilt, then fitted it with a Rolls-Royce *Merlin* aircraft engine. When finished it was unrecognizable from the boat we had taken delivery of in Vereeniging ten weeks before. The actual rebuilding was done by a young and energetic Englishman, Stan Martin, then of Vereeniging.

Miss X, more than any other South African boat, introduced high speed on the water to South Africa and created wide interest, particularly in the Transvaal. It led directly to the South African Gold Cup race, promoted by the Vaal Club. The Cup itself was donated by Bobby Bothner.

By late 1933 there were a number of people at Hythe who knew I was taking a keen interest in the study and design of fast hulls. Among them were Arnold Green, our works manager for a time; Wilf Pickerill; Ted Fox, another good friend of mine at the yard; and Les Still. But it was Arnold Green who was the first to mention to Aircraftman Shaw that I was attempting to break new ground in hull design and that I might be worthy of encouragement.

One day, Green, unknown to me, suggested to Shaw that he might like to act as test pilot and vet any craft that I might design and build. When Green told me what he had said to Shaw I was not only appalled, I was almost paralyzed by fright. As it turned out, I needn't have felt so stricken.

The next day Shaw stopped me in the yard, and urged me to keep on with what I was trying to do. He appeared to be very interested in my studies and said that he too had been giving some attention to the improvement of fast hull designs. He said that he would like to keep in touch with regard to my investigation and that perhaps he could help in some way if I thought fit. He then surprised me by mentioning, almost casually but nevertheless looking me straight in the eye, that it might be a good plan to treat my findings confidentially for the time being. He said no useful purpose would be served by openly discussing research work in progress, especially the kind of research the results of which might be found helpful for national defence. He then volunteered the wish that he would like, one day, to see "a new kind of British navy", one that would be the fastest and hardest-hitting in the world.

After this meeting in the open yard I gradually felt a responsibility I didn't want. The more I thought about what Shaw had said, the more worried I became. I didn't want to make a big thing of what I was trying to do. I just wanted to enjoy myself and linger lovingly over any discoveries I might make. I had no wish to be driven and no urgent desire for fame and fortune.

Within a few days, Shaw came early one morning to my office. I had just arrived at work and was in the act of uncovering my drawing board. He said he would like to exchange ideas with me. He talked of hull proportions, the amounts of V in the V-sections of existing types of hulls, engine-room and bridge layouts. All that he said was interesting, but it was obvious to me that he was thinking very much of the general improvements and refinements strictly along practical lines. My own thoughts were essentially theoretical. I was trying to make an "in depth" scientific approach and was not keen to waste time on the mere art of ship design.

He liked my thoughts on planing surfaces well enough to remark that, "I'm sure you're on to something there. If you can clean up the wake and its flow patterns, as you're suggesting, the hull's resistance will be reduced greatly".

We didn't talk for any length of time. We were on full display before the whole assembly bay. A further detriment to our privacy was the line of open, inter-office doorways linking my office to that on each side of me. This line controlled the common pathway for communication along the single floor of the three offices; foremen and office-workers were continually ambling or hurrying backward and forward along it.

When Shaw had gone, I once again began to wonder what I might be letting myself in for. Could I keep pace with him? Would I get out of my depth? Through it all, I had a strong feeling that Shaw was sizing me up and, though I felt flattered to be under his observation, I doubted my fitness to be anything but what I was, a contented and conscientious plodder out to enjoy himself.

As I was so often to learn during my association with Shaw, I should not have been alarmed. I believe he sensed my feelings and so acted toward me that I came to regard him as I would anyone else I worked with. He never attempted to dictate or dominate. But, deep down, I never lost sight of the fact that Shaw was a famous man in his own right and that his privilege of association was all mine. I took no liberties and carefully toed the line I had chalked out for myself. I don't think I ever over-stepped it.

Without consciously working it out in my mind to do so (it should be remembered that I was young, no philosopher and merely a design craftsman with a bent for improving mechanisms) I sensed that I ought to listen as intelligently as I could to all that Shaw might tell me of his ideas. Further, should his interest continue, I ought to do my best to convert his ideas, as well as my own, into sound mathematical theory and, if ever given the chance, into top-notch hardware. Quite a resolve! But there again, I was young, a little brash and, as yet, undefeated in my reach.

I felt that Shaw's ideas for a new kind of British Navy (as he so simply put it) would be conditioned by his mastery of military strategy and tactics. In this I was right. This knowledge kept showing up so regularly in our talks, and so weightily, that I too began to interest myself in the subjects. Some years later, I even managed to continue my war studies at university level.

On the evening of the day that we first talked in my office about our ideas, just before going to bed, I made a short list of the things we had discussed and, for the moment, I left it at that. I more than half-hoped Shaw would turn luke-warm and leave me to my own serene and steady progress. I would have liked that; but again, I should have known better. He continued to show a steady interest in all that I did.

This led me to the belief that it would be a good idea to find a more secluded office, one where we could talk without being noticed or overheard. Such an opportunity presented itself when suitable space became unexpectedly vacant in what had been a small house near the main entrance to the yard. Furthermore, to our advantage, it was not directly facing the general office block. I quickly arranged possession of a room in the house by sweet-talking our general manager, S.N. Barker, into the change. He looked upon me with favour at this time.

The office was on the upper floor of the cottage, up a bare wooden staircase. It had been a bedroom in the past. There was a small landing at the top of the stairs and on the landing there were two doors facing each other. One led into my office, the other into Ted Fox's. Ted's office was similar to mine but his was always busy. I had a window in the wall opposite the door and, as it was north-facing, I kept it free of curtains and placed my board in front of it. To my left, as I sat at the board, at right angles to it, I put my long reference table. This table was constructed like a thin-planked outhouse door, with cross-battens underneath it. It was long, bare of finish and flexible under load. It rested loosely on two carpenter's trestles. On it I spread my longer drawings.

The new office turned out to be ideal for my purposes and, as Les Still remained in the assembly bay office, I was left quiet and undisturbed for most of my time. As I worked solely on experimental and advance development projects for Power Boat, there was little need to discuss my ideas with Scotty every day, and then not in my office but in his. I rarely saw Barker.

It was in this office that most of my talks with Shaw took place. And it was on this reference table, with the drawings folded once-over in order to make space, that he sat, legs crossed, the thin table-top flexing under his weight.

I recollect only one occasion when he ignored this table as a bench to sit on. The reason, he said, was because he had a sore backside, caused by painful boils which ran across his shoulders and down his back to his buttocks. I suggested he take a couple of spoonfuls of brewer's yeast every day. I spoke from sad experience and told him so. I had had a bad crop of these painful sores on the back of my neck during my late Coventry and early Bourne days. So that day Shaw stood as we talked and, out of sympathy, so did I.

Whenever Shaw was with me and a visitor walked in – it could be anyone from a yard apprentice to friendly manufacturer's representative – he would, without a word, quietly disappear. He was an expert at this manoeuvre and, as a result, I never once had need to attempt an introduction. Knowing something of his nature, I felt a kind of relief to find him gone by the time my greeting to the newcomer was over.

I knew for certain that Shaw was in or about the yard whenever I saw his motorcycle parked just inside the main entrance. His habit was to park it opposite my small building on the loose, chipped-granite surface to one side of the Goods Received building. On occasion, he made the journey from his digs in Southampton, not by the long road on his motorcycle, but on foot and by ferryboat to Hythe pier, then by the pier tramway to the high street. It was only a few minutes' walk past the few shops and pubs to the yard gates. At other times he would be picked up in Southampton by one of our own power dinghies and ferried direct to the yard's jetty.

I never made a practice of searching for Shaw in our yard; I thought it too noticeable and rather risky, in our tight little world. I soon came to know that he would seek me out whenever he had something to say.

On one visit to my office, only to find me absent, he placed the long stick of my beam compass diagonally across my board. Underneath the stick and nipped down by it, face down, was a sheet from his pocket book. It showed a simple but neat sketch of a new idea in hull cross-sections. The lines were drawn in pencil and the notes written in ink. His visits to my office were without fuss or greeting. As I too was not one for introductory small talk, this suited me very well.

Few people could have taken special heed of Shaw's visits to my office. They were by no means regular and each could have represented, as some did, his keen interest in his liaison duties on behalf of the R.A.F. I was kept busy designing new equipment for use in the near and distant future. Much of what I was doing for Power Boat in general would, sooner or later, be installed in the R.A.F. craft we were constantly striving to improve. It was part of his job to know how much progress was being made in any on-going design and development programme which might become a feature of an R.A.F. boat, and to know when any particular piece of experimental hardware would be ready for ocean test.

After a few months in my cottage office I began to wonder if Ted Fox, who was our advertising manager, photographer and public relations officer, had guessed that there was something going on between Shaw and me. Ted was, after all, located right on my office door-step. But he gave no inkling that he might be curious about the purpose of Shaw's and my quiet talks. I can only think that had Ted really become aware of our scientific curiosity outside Power Boat then he had, as a good friend of mine, been kind enough to ignore the matter completely. He was a busy, tireless young man, with little time for unimportant distractions; for which I was thankful.

Later, however, others did have their suspicions and these surfaced openly, though quietly, in the mid-summer of 1934. Luckily, by this time, although Shaw and I did not know it, our more active association was drawing to a close.

It was at this time that – our manager, S.N. Barker, working, I feel sure, to instructions from above – invited me out for a pleasant country drive and a gentlemanly pub crawl. I went along, certain in my own mind that I was about to be pumped in earnest. So I was not at all surprised to find myself subjected, casually but determinedly, to friendly questioning about my spare-time activities.

I took no offence at this probing; it was a lovely summer evening and I wanted to enjoy my outing – I had no car of my own. I took pains to talk as a mechanical engineer, not as a naval architect. Whenever Shaw's name came up, I filibustered. I spoke long and earnestly about his thoroughbred motorcycle and the expert way in which he handled it. Being by nature a simpleton, I had no great difficulty in acting like one.

A couple of weeks later I was again entertained, but this time it was at Barker's home, with his wife present. We had an excellent dinner and a very pleasant evening. I serenely endured a similar kind of questioning to that which I had fended off before and with a similar result even though, on this occasion, it was strongly hinted that there was talk of Shaw, me, and some kind of new boat.

Shaw and I had good reason for, if not cloak-and-dagger secrecy, sober caution. I needed my job and Shaw needed to avoid sensational controversy and publicity. The latter, whenever it surfaced, never failed to reach the ears and eyes of the higher authorities in the RAF and to annoy them.

Just before I first met Shaw, he had borne unwelcome publicity from the press because of his work with our target boats. These boats he had piloted while being practice-bombed from the air with tiny bombs and chalk bags. But the truth about the practice runs had been exaggerated and sensationalized much beyond his and the RAF's liking.

For my part, I tried hard to keep up the appearance of living a normal and uncomplicated life; but it became increasingly more difficult to do so and, at the same time, put in the extra hours that, more and more, my investigations demanded. Wilf Pickerill and Arnold Green were closest to me at Power Boat, but even they did not suspect how deeply I had become involved either with Shaw or the actual theoretical research I was doing. For such a novice in the art of subterfuge, I had learned to cover the closeness of our talks with some competency.

One of my most useful subterfuges for gaining further time for study, without arousing suspicion, was the pretence of taking catnaps at every opportunity. This habit openly amused my closer friends and became a continuing joke among them. On the bus and on the tramcar, on the ferry and on the train, in the theatre and in the pub, at dinner and at supper, I would, the moment the opportunity arose, close my eyes and drop my chin on to my chest. In such a pose, I could shut off my mind to all that was going on around me. This wasn't difficult to do. It needed minimal practice. I became adept at picturing in my mind a new idea in most of its possible forms and, sometimes, even a complete design, in fairly close detail. Further, my ability to perform mental arithmetic and to approximate solutions to complicated mathematical problems improved tremendously.

Devotion to work and to long hours might be repulsive virtues and hard labour might be a slow and sure killer, but one has only to look around to see that Fortune favours the industrious. And I was, by any of the usual man-made standards, industrious to a fault – frenziedly and happily so. I suffered only the unused-to stress of silence; although, even in this respect, my maverick nature was no hindrance.

Shaw, although not a professional engineer – he was, by earlier training, an archaeologist – needed no spoon-feeding in anything to do with mechanical engineering at any level. Further, he was easy to work with. I never felt ill at ease with him, partly I think, because he never attempted to overpower me. Unlike Lord Macaulay, of whom Sidney Smith wrote, "He not only overflowed with learning, but stood in the slop", Shaw was careful to tune his learning to suit my limited capacity for absorbing it. His comments were a delight to hear: simple, direct and explicit. From the start I admired tremendously his choice of word and expression. His comment on my planing surface goal was Euclidian in its simplicity and clarity. He summed up what I had taken ten minutes to explain, with, "Yes! You must leave your wake as clean as the water surface immediately ahead of you". He always pin-pointed what it was I was trying to say or do.

Shaw's sketches were neat and clear. Each line spoke its purpose well enough, no deciphering was needed to translate the message it intended. Two of his sketches I kept by me for many years. To my regret they got left in Bradford when I emigrated from England soon after the Second War. One of them showed a proposed multi-engined power plant installation, together with its appropriate propeller drives. The other showed the geometry of a multi-rudder scheme that would match the suggested power plant layout of the first sketch.

At an early stage in our talks I began the habit of writing a brief report covering any findings I might have developed or unearthed relating to the ideas and problems we had discussed on a previous occasion. Shaw would respond to my technical notes by urging further work on any ideas that showed promise of practical fulfilment. My own research interests, remained strongly theoretical. Shaw always focused his mind on the possible direct application of theory. It was no hardship for me to work effectively toward both goals.

Whenever I put forward a set of facts or developed a theory that would settle a particular investigation to his satisfaction, he would term the solution a *special* or a *general* one. The choice of classification depended upon whether it could be used solely for a new kind of high-speed boat that we ourselves might develop or whether it could be used for a contemporary design of speedboat, *á la* existing RAF/British Power Boat pattern. To give a practical rather than a theoretical example: our final form of power transmission was termed general because it was universal in its possible applications; but our method of releasing torpedoes was classed as special, because it was practicable only to our own unique form of hull.

Over the eleven months of our direct talks I filled seven school exercise books with new theories and calculations of all kinds. The entries were summaries of what had been lengthier works of mine. A lot of the entries covered my work on new planing and control surface theory; surface friction and hydrodynamic theory; balance diagrams; new forms of lower hull geometry; aerodynamics and the upper hull; proposed future experiments of a laboratory nature; design proposals for new kinds of test equipment; general design sketches for improvements in the more important ship's components;

45

and many analytical and estimated performance tabulations for further research guidance.

These notebooks became invaluable to me during the years 1935-37. But, even as early in our work as September 1934, they demonstrated convincing proof that together we had made important theoretical progress, far ahead of what was then being contemplated in the industry itself. The maritime nations of the world took more than twenty-five years to reach the stage we had reached by the time of Shaw's untimely death in May, 1935. A further twenty-five years passed for our elliptical rudder to be accepted. It is now used on most of the America's Cup racing yachts where minimum resistance is critically important.

Shaw visited me one warm, still afternoon and, after seating himself on my reference table and talking for only a couple of minutes, suddenly closed his eyes and dozed off. Afraid he would roll forward off the table, I gently touched his knee to rouse him. It was the only time I ever touched him. He came to instantly and said he had been up all the previous night writing letters. Regular hours, I soon found out, meant little to him.

As late as January, 1935 when my investigations had, in major theory at least, reached their final stages and we had both left British Power Boat, Shaw wrote me from Bridlington, where he was on his last assignment before retiring from the RAF. Besides mentioning his coming retirement, he referred to the kinds of boats that were still being delivered to the RAF naval service. He said, "I feel that engines – petrol engines – are at very nearly their best: that hulls are only in their beginnings, and propellers hardly even that. There is plenty of room for research indeed!"

He further stated, "Our 37½ foot boats are about as far as planing displacement hulls have yet gone: that is, they are a pretty level compromise between speed, cost and seaworthiness. Twenty years hence, I hope something very different will rule."

That hope was not to be in vain. There were indeed to be some differences, many of these differences were to be ones spawned by the ideas he himself had helped so clearly to forecast in our talks of 1933 and 1934.

Chapter 4: A Ship and a Dream

I had begun my theoretical investigations for the improvements in the design of high speed boats out of natural enthusiasm and with the thought that I should, in due course, thoroughly enjoy the necessary physical experiments to prove whatever theories I came up with. My investigations, after two weeks of primitive blitzkrieg, were to have been a long-term activity, full of pleasure and interest. Only vaguely did I consider the possibility of the wide application of any of my ideas. But talking with Shaw had gradually brought me under the spell of the grand dream he cherished for "a new kind of British navy". So it came about that once I had grasped the full meaning and importance of this great dream, I did not hesitate to make it mine too, with the zeal and dedication of a religious convert.

The subterfuges I had to adopt to get through each day, although inconvenient, worried me little. For the best part of a year I enjoyed hearty laughter in good company and I went through the motions of taking my half-pint of "mild-and-bitter" with reasonable regularity. But I reflected inwardly more and more. My tongue, never very active, lost its meagre facility. I became more of a looker-on and my thinking never stopped. My maverick Gemini character enabled me to play this double game with ease. My sanity was rarely endangered by frustration.

By the beginning of May, 1934 I had built up a general but quite clear picture of what Shaw would like to see in a high-performance fighting ship of the future. This, together with the analytical work and sketch-pad brooding already recorded in my exercise books and on scraps of paper, gave me a flying start toward the final and most important part of our work, which was still out of view, but awaiting our whistle. The whistle itself, as we shall see, came as the result of a simple yet brilliant suggestion by Shaw.

My knowledge of naval architecture had improved rapidly and my mind, for once in my life, had soaked up and remembered all that I read and saw. This was for me a miracle of intellectual performance. The antics of water in motion fascinated me. I began to be impressed by my own mathematical approaches toward the confirmation of our new theories relating to the hydrodynamics of the high-speed ship. I noticed, with concealed glee, that Shaw readily accepted my technical explanations. I felt that I "belonged" and was approved as a co-worker of some competence.

Shaw's dream captivated me. He wanted to see developed an extremely fast, ocean-going fighting ship which had a displacement of as much as 1500 tons. Important features were to be great manoeuvrability, breath-taking acceleration and deceleration; small draft; low target profile; stalking silence; soft ride; long range; fuel economy through the inherent hydrodynamic efficiency of its hull and, very importantly, the ability to carry a high payload – no less than fifty percent of its gross displacement.

The possibility of high-speed tactics at sea, coupled with intense fire-power, fascinated him. This was clearly the reasoning of the experienced guerrilla leader. He constantly used such terms as: crushing attacks; armada thrashers; penetrator craft; sea tanks; and torpedo boat bashers. He talked about "a two-ocean fleet for the cost of one", and about "something new in high speed, sea-rescue hospitals".

I was content to let Shaw, a proved master in the art and science of major and minor strategy and battle tactics, determine the overall minimum design and performance specifications for our dream ship. My job became one of seeking and finding the best research and engineering paths to follow in order to satisfy his appetite for near-perfection. His quality standards for both performance and hardware would, I knew, be Rolls-Royce-like. Overnight I began to face those challenges with keen professional interest.

I now fancied myself as a fairly competent and blushingly responsible planing boat hydrodynamicist. Imagine my surprise to discover that when I talked to the fellows in the yard with a view to picking their brains about the finer points of a planing craft's running lines, they didn't seem to value my finicky queries. Their lukewarm interest did not embarrass me; instead I was pleased to recognize my own growing skills and sharpening observations.

Surprised as I might be at this sad professional backwardness, a yet bigger surprise awaited me, and Shaw. I came face to face with the full force and awesome effect of the square-cube law and how drastically it affected planing boat design. At that time this law was rarely considered by the industry with any seriousness. The boats it was then producing were drawing gingerly close to the limiting edge of the criteria where the law's damaging effects would be considerable. On rare occasions when the law *was* considered, it was treated lightly and a little doubtingly and fended off with chancy optimism. Today, of course, compliance with the square-cube law has become a serious and necessary tenet of the design process.

This vexing law tells us that there is a practical upper limit to the size and weight of a simple planing boat if it is to plane properly and attain a worthwhile performance while using a tolerable amount of propulsive effort.

It was clear to me that great changes would have to be made to existing designs to give Shaw even a modest part of all that he asked.

Just after he had returned from a lengthy visit to Henry Meadows, our engine builders in Wolverhampton, I brought this important observation to his attention. He had arrived back at the yard in excellent spirits but, when I told him my problem, he looked very disappointed. He had set his mind on new, fast ships up to the size of the destroyer and had said as much to his associates in the RAF, and to friends in the high-speed boat industry. Now this part of his dream looked as though it was shattered.

I went into the workings of the law for him, carefully and in detail. He soon realized that there was no easy way out. It could not be discreetly ignored and it could not be nonchalantly ducked.

The meaning of the square-cube law, as applied to the simple planing boat, is as follows:

A speedboat skims on the surface of the water; the bottom of the boat is the part on which the skimming takes place. The bottom surface is called its planing surface and varies in plan shape and cross-section from yard to yard, according to its designer's whim. Some planing surface shapes are more efficient than others. The important thing is that the *area* of this planing surface increases only as the *square* of the length of the boat, but the weight of the boat –

and this is the weight that the surface has to support against the reaction of the fast-moving water underneath it – increases as the *cube* of the length of the boat. More simply put this is saying that as the boat is made longer the weight of the boat increases at a higher rate than the length.

Imagine a solid cube of hard, smooth material, with a side-length of one foot, and another cube of similar material with a side-length of four feet. If the first cube weighs, say, one pound, then the second cube will weigh 64-pounds. The area of one face of the small cube will be one square foot, whereas that of the large cube will be sixteen square feet. If the two cubes were resting in water, the weight on each square foot of the resting surface would be one pound for the small cube, and four pounds for the large cube. The loading on each square foot of the face of the large cube is four times more intense than that on the small cube.

For each cube to skim or plane on one of its faces and support its own weight – as a speedboat does – the larger cube would need to travel on the surface of the water (at a slight inclination to it) at twice the speed of the smaller. The power required to propel it at that speed would be 128 times greater.

I further explained this to Shaw by taking British Power Boat's 37½ -ft. express cruiser – a craft we both knew well – and comparing it through the square-cube law with an imaginary craft of similar design, but four times larger. Our Power Boat was powered by two engines, each developing 100 horse power; when sea conditions were good it reached a top speed of 45 mph. I showed him that, for a practical comparison of performance, the top speed of the longer craft of 150-ft. would need to reach 90 mph and that the power needed for its propulsion at that speed would be 25,600 hp. At that time, 1934, such a large amount of power would have been almost impossible to engineer in a light enough package.

After this detailed explanation I did not see Shaw for the better part of a week. When I did, he solemnly tackled me with the challenge, "Well, Spurr! What can you do? Is there a loophole?" I had had time to think hard, and replied, "Yes! We can do some bamboozling." At this remark he looked astonished. Then, suddenly, he grinned like a schoolboy and declared, "You've come to the right chap for that!" He then told me that Julius Caesar once said that facts cannot be altered, but that they can be manipulated and re-arranged and to that extent controlled.

This, then, was what our task demanded of us; and this was what, finally, we accomplished and with a much greater degree of success than we had, at the earlier disappointed stage, expected. We came, not to disprove or to duck the square-cube law, but to fool it, and so delay its adverse effect upon our plans to the point where it would cause us no undue embarrassment for, perhaps, the next twenty-five years.

And so it came about that from then onward, with the help of Caesar's wisdom and our philosophical bamboozling, we not only manipulated to good effect the facts and theories we had already come up with, but began to apply similar treatment to a new and revolutionary thought which had begun to excite us almost to the point of open ecstasy. This thought was one that would enable me to fashion our hull in such a way that it would provide considerable, yet low cost, air lift.

Our machinations were applied to the following list of goals we were so diligently seeking; it was the last item on our list which, by jiggery-pokery, would lead us well into the future and then extend our ideas for use, as will be seen, well beyond our own lifetime:

I would continue my search to make our planing surfaces more efficient than those already in use. That is, I would increase their lift and reduce drag.

I would reduce considerably the construction weight of the hull by using an improved, all-metal, aircraft kind of construction; and I would apply advanced aircraft design practice to every mechanical item throughout the craft.

I would not hesitate to use exotic materials in order to reduce weight or improve the strength of any component.

I would reduce the weight of the complete power plant installation and its power transmission system by careful attention to layout and detail design.

I would, as a means toward improving the craft's overall lift-to-drag ratio, reduce the appendage drag – that is, reduce the resistance of those parts dangling in the water – to an ideal minimum.

I would preserve the optimum balance of the hull at all speeds for minimum drag.

I would keep the size of any necessary superstructure on the hull as small and as cleanly shaped as possible in order to reduce parasitic drag.

I would, finally make the hull, by virtue of its shape and by its motion through the air when underway, do its fair share in helping to lift the weight of the craft.

Shaw and I judged that any success along this final path of research would demonstrate organized cheating of the highest scientific order (short of a no-cost means of levitation) against the crippling effect of the square-cube law. Air was cheaper than water in terms of lift-to-drag ratio and we should have far less parasitic drag for the craft as a whole.

About the only phenomena we couldn't control and modify were sea and weather conditions. These, we decided in our magnanimity, would have to be accepted with a seaman's grace.

Should all these innovations be accomplished with proper efficiency, the new ship could be made to do more useful work at less energy cost than conventionally designed vessels; and valuable gains in load-carrying ability and top speed would be won.

With these thoughts in mind we both breathed easier. Shaw was now placated and, once again, optimistic; but from this time forward his conversation showed that his horizon had closed in. He now thought of his dream ship as a 150-footer at most. The immediate possibility of a 300-footer had faded. He left me to determine the limiting gross displacement which our new system would permit in order to get the high performances on which he had set his heart.

Our talks were never regular or predetermined. Shaw would visit me only when he had an interesting thought to impart. Sometimes he would be away from the yard for days on end. On two occasions, when he took trips along the coast, his absence was much longer. In June, I think it was, he made working cruises as far as Plymouth and Bridlington. Most of his visits to me were brief; but he always left me with something to ponder.

It was his habit to give a single tap on my door and walk straight in. The door was left open; but he talked quietly. He would fold over the long drawings on my reference table and sit on the bared portion with his legs crossed, sometimes slowly swinging them. His hands clasped the edge of the table, giving him a slight lean forward. In that position, after I had made a quarter turn on my stool, he would be looking directly at me. In this way he would talk and I would sometimes sketch.

Between us, mainly from Shaw's prompting and my toil, we had broken a lot of new ground and I began to get the satisfied feeling that our work would have done credit to a national research institution. A list of our completed work, written up in early June, showed big strides in theoretical investigations and in major component design and geometry; but complete ship and envelope shapes, though vaguely envisaged, were still not clear.

My new principles and theoretical proofs were mounting in importance; it would soon be necessary to conduct the related model experiments that were essential to support these principles and theoretical proofs. We had no idea how this could be done. There were no facilities available which we could afford to use; simple towing tests seemed primitive and inaccurate. Shaw mentioned that it might be possible to get help from the National Physical Laboratory at Teddington. But to take that course would mean obtaining a grant of some kind and, therefore, a full disclosure of all that we were up to. He never talked about this move again. We were both intensely independent and were subconsciously reluctant to give up control of our child to a lot of pale, indistinct faces seated around a long, polished table.

Later in June, Ted Fox asked if I would vet a used car, which a friend of his was wondering whether or not to buy. I forget the name of his friend, but recollect that he was editor and publisher of the *Dairy Farmer*. We all met at the dealer's showroom in Southampton and then took the car into the countryside for a good run. After some simple tests the car, a Wolsley *Hornet* sports model, was pronounced to be in good condition. My task completed and being by that time near Bucklers Hard, I was overcome by a strong urge to visit the place and, on my own, meditate for a while. I don't know whether it was the lovely summer day, the effect of the countryside on me, or some deeper feeling, but the urge was compelling. Accordingly, excusing myself, I left Ted and his friend and walked to the Hard.

The late afternoon was still warm, so I sat in the open air near the old stocks where a sister ship to Nelson's *Victory* had been built in the late eighteenth century.

I pondered and sketched for twenty minutes, perfectly content. There was no one about. I heard only the occasional sound of a passing vehicle. The trees were still and the water surface before me was smooth as glass.

Suddenly, without the warning sound of footsteps – the verge where I was sitting was grassland – a voice behind me said, quietly, "Have you watched a ship's anchor during a free plunge?"

I turned to see Shaw standing near. Surprised, I failed to answer immediately so he continued, "It doesn't weave from side to side like a penny. Down it goes, whoosh! Straight as an arrow." I didn't mention that I would have guessed as much. Instead I asked him how on earth he had discovered such a profound scientific secret. He said, "By simple experiment! Yesterday morning, ten minutes out from the yard, with a new bo'sun's mate as companion, the dinghy's engine died on me. I began to look for the trouble, so the new boy swung the anchor overboard." He paused, then added lightly, "The end of the line wasn't attached to the dinghy."

Shaw went on to tell me that when he caught sight of me he was trundling along on his motorbike, looking for a bottle of lemonade and a quiet spot to drink it.

He asked how I was getting along with my Rupert Brooke. He had given me a copy of Brooke's *Poems* the previous month. I later discovered that he had bought the copy for me at a used-book shop in Southampton, a shop we both knew. He had done so for no other reason than the chance remark I had made that Brooke appealed to me. I told him I was just then enjoying *The Fish*, and a couple of the other experimental poems of shorter length.

Months after I left Hythe for good, kindly disposed Les Still complemented this copy of Shaw's by forwarding me Brooke's *1914 and Other Poems*. These slender volumes bring back happy memories of a world that has now passed us by, a world that I liked and loved very much.

For a short time Shaw and I talked about the new forward and reverse gearbox, which I was then designing and building for Scotty. Many of the parts were nearing completion. I told him that some of the assembly work would be tricky especially when we came to fit the taper-backed, bevel reduction gears into their split cage. He remarked that Munro, our chief mechanic, was a good man and that the final assembly "Will be just as you want it, Spurr".

Suddenly, without a hint of any kind, came the breakthrough that made my exercise book theories and calculations come to life as a family. Each lost it separateness.

Shaw, in a quiet voice, said, "Mechanically and fluidically, the planing boat is an aeroplane".

I think this simple though profound thought had been near the conscious level in our mind for weeks; but as so often happened in our talks, it was Shaw who said it first. The clear meaning of what he said hit me like a hammer. Everything I had done in our research together crystallized into a whole and at last I felt there were no loose ends fragmenting our quest.

The thought was not merely stating once again that, in the design of the speedboat, light weight was of the utmost importance. That fact had already been recognized by Scott-Paine in the construction of *Miss Britain III*. Rather, the idea focused the mind on the fact that the design-parallel of the high-speed planing boat and aeroplane was a complete one: the mass of knowledge already established in the aeronautical field might be used, with some notational changes, in the other.

I couldn't get away from Shaw fast enough. I wanted to think. On my way home I resolved, by way of confirmation, to compare all the work I had done on the planing surface with the documented and well understood aerodynamic laws and equations of the aeroplane wing. If I was able to demonstrate the validity of this special parallel by finding correlations that would permit me to transform one set of data into the other, and to express in a similar kind of notation, then I could move with confidence from the special to the general parallel, in accordance with Shaw's thinking. With the confirmation of a general parallel, short cuts would be possible which could, directly and painlessly, lead to solutions of most of the theoretical and practical problems encountered in the design, construction and development of a supership.

From this one thought alone, so simply put by Shaw, and so relentlessly pursued by me, we garnered a rich and royal harvest.

Perhaps the ship and the dream were now approaching reality.

Chapter 5: The Supership is Born

Without much mathematical juggling on my part, I soon found that it was indeed possible to show that the forces and moments acting on a planing surface could be represented by relationships similar to those acting on an aerofoil and that they could be expressed in the terms and forms of aerodynamics.

Shaw and I were delighted with this sudden breakthrough. It made it easier for me to say just what I meant. For months I had been taxing my comparatively newly-found mathematical genius in struggling to define accurately my observations, theories and geometries of the planing surface.

After this success with the special case of the planing surface, it became but another short step to show that the general theory also was valid. Further analytical comparisons were made for surface friction, form drag, stability and balance, fin effects, control surfaces, origin and development of dynamic loads and all cases of performance. The results were convincing. From that time forward a sixth-form schoolboy could handle the mathematics of our work. All that was needed was a good, straightforward, textbook on aircraft design at one's elbow. But the biggest windfall that fell at our feet directly from the new technique was the gift of being able to see the new form and layout that our supership needed to take for best total performance.

This great step forward in our work came about directly from Shaw's simple observation of the strong parallel of the high-speed planing boat and the aeroplane. Years later, the thought *did* strike me as to why on earth we had taken so long to discover this easy pathway to success. It was not, I think, as Dr. Johnson once admitted, pure ignorance, but rather that we had been negligent in the reading of our own early documented signals which so clearly forecast the phenomenon.

Shaw liked our new analogical approach so much, and considered it to be so important, that he suggested I prepare a paper outlining our theories and the methods we had adopted to establish and develop them. He said I was the one to give it before the Royal

Institution of Naval Architects or the Royal Aeronautical Society but that he would be pleased to help me write its final form. Accordingly, I did some work on the paper, as a pencil draft, although I never completed it. My mind was on more exciting things. I was a dedicated designer not a teacher or enlightener. To write my part of the paper would have taken up valuable time and would have been an uninteresting, boring chore. As for delivering it before an august society of professional critics, I think I would have wetted myself. I have never been able to take any pleasure in holding forth before an audience. When I was much older and had even become a dignified member of council, I did write the paper and give it before the Royal Aeronautical Society, in South Africa. But more of that later.

With the aid of our new analogical approach I was already beginning to visualize the form and layout of an actual craft of advanced kind. I made many thumbnail sketches before reaching what I thought would be, with a few minor variations, a good general solution.

One day in July, Shaw and I met by chance on our slipway at Scotty's yard. Together we strolled toward the large storage building to which he had been making his way. As we moved across the warm, sunlit concrete, I glanced over the dazzling blue Solent and saw in the far distance two boats moored close to each other. The contrast between them was poetic. One was a white, graceful, J Class racing yacht, with its towering, rapier-like mast reaching for the sky; the other was the famed greyhound and clipper ship of the high seas, the legendary, black hulled, *Cutty Sark*. It was a sight to remember.

My head was full of the sketch-layouts I had been making of what, in my enthusiasm and conceit, I told myself were wonder-boats. Most designers tend to preen themselves in this way after working long hours on a new design which, finally, begins to look as good as they would like it to be. I was no exception to this kind of day dreaming. It is a pleasant and ego-satisfying temporary deception; one to be recommended if sanity and vocational cheerfulness are to be preserved in a mostly dull and routine world.

As we walked along the concrete I controlled my vain satisfaction remarkably well. I spoke to Shaw very quietly, almost in the form of a soliloquy. Looking sideways at him as he looked down, I said, "Mr. Shaw, what do you think of the idea of a large planing boat, based on our best findings, and designed on the constructional principles of an all-metal flying boat? It would carry a main, broad, planing surface almost amidships and a much narrower, auxiliary, planing surface aft. The basic hull would take the form of an aerofoil section with a straight bow, not a V-shaped one, and so be capable of developing appreciable air lift when under way. The centre of gravity would be engineered to be over the main planing surface. An integrated and streamline engine-transmission-propeller system would be installed at the centre of gravity location, and a dagger-shaped rudder blade would be mounted as far aft as possible, under the auxiliary planing surface. The general form of the hull assembly, together with all external components and excrescences above and below the water-line, would be of streamline shape and smooth. The balance of forces about the centre of gravity of the boat would be identical in principle with that of a flying boat just before take-off."

Shaw listened carefully to all I said, but passed no immediate comment. I sensed, however, from the expression on his face, that the configuration had its appeal. He slowed his slow walk almost to a stop as the image of the boat continued to refine itself in his mind. After what seemed to be quite a time, he drew to a standstill and, looking at the ground for a second, said, "Spurr, you've got it. It's a good plan. Why don't you make some sketches of the craft, showing it in perspective?" He suggested I make sketches of two boats: a 100-ft. torpedo boat, as a starter for our fight against the square-cube law; and a racing boat, as a direct comparison of our principles with those of Scotty's *Miss Britain III*. I said I would do this.

Shaw found what he was looking for in the storage shed – a newly delivered small diesel engine – and made a few notes as I looked on. Then, with my help, he threw a heavy dust cover over a short line of dinghy engines which had caught his eye and were getting dust laden.

On our return we talked of other things. One topic was Noel Coward's *Cavalcade*. I cannot remember whether or not he said he knew Coward, but he did say that he had seen the film and liked it. He also hinted that my humour had something of Mark Twain's in it, and that I might make an effort to develop it. I don't know where he got that idea.

The afternoon was growing late and I had not drunk any of my tea from my very small flask, so we shared it. Shaw remarked that it was "a drop of sergeant major's". I told him I had got to like strong tea through my father, who in turn had got it from Private Thompson, his army pal, an assistant regimental postman. When I told Shaw that my father had been one of the first volunteers to join the 18th West Yorkshire Regiment, he amazed me by saying that regiment had been stationed in Egypt for a short while in 1915 and that its emblem was a white horse at full gallop. He was right! What a memory.

Tea over, Shaw took his leave. He was never a lingerer. Within a few seconds I heard him kick-start his motorbike and then came the burble of the big engine. With a beautifully controlled roar from the big Brough Superior, V-twin engined motorbike, he was on his way. I think his Brough was his fiery stallion or gentle doe, depending on his mood. I'm sure he thought of it very much as did King Arthur his valiant charger. He kept this machine, a 1932 model SS100, in spotless condition and in fine tune. It was a beautiful machine, the envy of any motorcycle connoisseur of that period.

After he had gone, I covered my drawing board with its dust sheet and wended my way home to my digs. After my evening meal I continued my reading of Jerome's *Three Men in a Boat* and, at the same time, attempted to review my thoughts of the afternoon's talk. It had been a rewarding half-hour for me. At 7.30 pm, on a surging impulse, I began to sketch.

I drew some quick picture-views of the torpedo boat and the racing boat, for Shaw to look at when we next met. At this same sitting, without a single break as if inspired by a heavenly compulsion, I sketched a series of sixty-eight model hull forms to be built in the future for test purposes. This series, with no key additions or deletions, was to demonstrate the breadth and density of

60

our theoretical work and to show the evolutionary path taken from the existing art to the supership. It was a sudden Darwinian-inspired effort on my part and, looking back, a remarkable one. This order of progression remained true in its concept for more than thirty years, until such time when another and greater breakthrough evolved from it, which took the earlier, basic supership into the space-age era. The later breakthrough has never been disclosed; and probably never will. It was 5.30 am the next day when the spirit of the demon left me and I went to bed for two hours, weary beyond recall, my mind then dull and spent. But our work was now consolidated. It was made clear and precise.

Sometime later a simple reference-hull was added to the series, at Shaw's suggestion, and placed in the first position on our test programme. It was for the purpose of direct test-reference only and was added for routine and practical reasons. Nevertheless its value was important and unique. It will be referred to again in the right place. So, finally, there were sixty-nine models to be made and tested.

A day or two later Shaw saw what I had done. At the first sight of the torpedo boat sketch, he said, "Let's call it *Crusader*." In the same breath he insisted that it was "screaming for a spring bottom of some kind". Then came the quiet, but none-the-less firm, pressure question, "Can anything be done about it?" Subsequently, and to his delight, I came up with a design for supporting the larger part of the boat's weight on a torsion bar suspension system, attached to the main planing surface and to the two-full depth, girder-type keelsons which ran along the length of the hull. It looked good. It was a scheme that was later patented.

Always in Shaw's mind was the valid conviction that the kind of craft we were trying to evolve could also form the basis for a successful family of moderately large, high speed ships suitable for commercial and express passenger-cruiser duties. In the latter case the final design would have to demonstrate, first and foremost, a marriage of speed and comfort. He was emphatic about this combination and considered it to be essential for the success of a passenger-carrying craft. The new spring bottom I had devised clinched the deal; it fitted his conception perfectly. He was delighted to think that we had achieved this important advance without detriment to the efficiency of the new planing surface. We had, he said, taken a major step toward breaking the top-speed/hard-ride syndrome of the speedboat. Later, in 1936, I dubbed the express passenger cruiser *Merry England.*

The sketch I had made of the racing boat pleased him immensely. It did a good job of displaying all the innovations embodied in our design. He looked at it for a long time, then he described the lines as being "beautifully sleek". He told me "Projection for projection, and line for line, it's cleaner than Reg Mitchell's S.6b." The S.6b was the seaplane, built by Vickers Supermarine, that won for Britain in 1931 the prized Schneider Trophy. This aircraft remains, even today (it can be seen in the Science Museum at Kensington), a very fine example of aeronautical cleanliness. I valued this complement from Shaw, its spontaneity and its directness, made me feel good. Shaw, as a liaison man, had seen much of the Schneider Trophy aircraft during the 1929 races off the Isle of Wight. He had learned to recognize a good set of lines.

Furthermore, Shaw was openly appreciative of my sketches for the sixty-eight test models. The Darwinian approach intrigued him; he went over them again and again. He checked the evolutionary pattern from one to the other, all the way up the tree, to our final layout prediction as shown by the two sketches drawn in perspective.

A few days after this session, on his next visit to my office, I demonstrated the practical possibilities of the ground-effect phenomenon. I did this by holding down a simply folded paper aerofoil on a thick piece of cardboard sheet with the tip of my pencil. I then placed the cardboard in a horizontal position in the air-stream delivered from my room fan. He saw the air lift take place as I gradually eased the load on the pencil tip. When he tried it himself he was quick to notice that the best effect was when the gap was small. It was a tricky experiment, we kept losing control of the aerofoil; but the test served the purpose for the time being.

After that walk along Power Boat's slipway in July, when we had discussed the sketches I had made, we knew fairly clearly for the first time what, in general, our boats were going to look like. We then began to turn our thoughts toward the final details of the

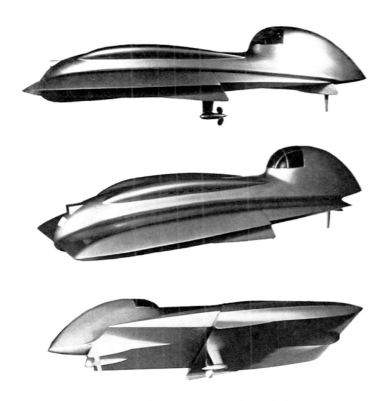

Empire Day II model

*Note (a), the overall aerofoil shape of the hull to provide lift,
with its straight leading edge; (b) the streamlined bulbs on the
fuselage to house the larger engine; (c), the aerodynamic tail
fin housing the cockpit; (d), underneath the bow, the 'wave-
splitter' vestige of a V-hull, as advised by Shaw; (e) the step
between the main planing surface and the after surface to
reduce the wetted area and hence frictional drag; (f), the
novel, minimum-drag propeller drive on a leg; (g), the
'inwash' fins to contain the spray and air under the main
planing surface; (h), the long, narrow elliptical blade of the
rudder; (i), the twin hydrodynamic skegs complementing the
tail fin.*

63

structural and mechanical design features, already generalized in my exercise books, and toward thoughts on model-testing, based on the programme I had devised during my all-night marathon drawing session.

After I had made several small-scale layouts of the torpedo boat, showing relatively minor variations in proportion, my first task was to allay Shaw's genuine fear of a too frail, light alloy construction for the hull. He visualized serious failures resulting from skin drumming, owing to the possibility of diaphragm effects between the frames. No structure is completely rigid, and he was much concerned about consequent distortions that could bring about severe stress effects throughout the hull's skin, not to mention the dread of rivets popping free in a heavy sea. This indeed was a problem and I spent much time reviewing my sketches and proposals.

It should be noted, in this connection, that every bit of the design work, from the very beginning, and all the figure work for the theory, had been done in pencil, mostly in exercise books, and that all layouts were small-scale and drawn free-hand. Not until October, 1934, did I begin accurate layout work, and that was at Bradford, my old home-town.

Before long I developed a practical lightweight design for the skin, one that offered us confidence rather than alarm. It came in the form of a sandwich construction. Nipped between two sheets of light alloy, to stabilize them and give them bulk and cemented to both, was a hard, ultra-lightweight, expanded-rubber panel, three inches thick. It was intended that these compound sheets would be pre-fabricated. The joints themselves were so designed that they made an extremely rigid structural member of the hull. Looking back, this system could possibly be seen as a forerunner of the modern honeycomb sandwich, used so successfully today by aircraft manufacturers.

At the time when we were discussing rudder blades, Shaw noted that among contemporary designs there appeared to be no standard shape of blade agreed by naval architects as best suitable for the fast-bottomed speedboat. It struck him as odd that designs varied so widely when, generally, the blade was operating in an unobstructed stream of water. Of all those he had seen, "not one of them looked right". He believed that a rudder blade was a simple component to idealize. He put the usual action question to me, "Can something be done about it?" and, "Why not give it some original thought? Work it out from the beginning!"

The aircraft analogy applied beautifully. I didn't need to be a genius to find a solution. Within a day or two of his request, I had extended my dagger blade idea and proposed an elliptical plan-form blade of high aspect ratio with streamline cross-sections at all stations across the blade. I also proposed that the blade root be faired into a flat turntable, flush with the rear planing surface, to avoid eddy-making resistance between blade and boat's bottom. I straightened the centre of pressure line of the blade by juggling the basic geometry of the elliptical form and then arranged this line so that it became a continuation of the rudder-stock centre line. With this modification to the geometry, the hand load needed at the steering wheel became negligible and blade twist was avoided in the very slender blade.

This new form of blade was later patented. It was patented both as a rudder blade for speedboats and as the most efficient aeroplane wing for subsonic flight. This geometry was eventually applied to the *Spitfire* wing: its shape became a recognition factor for aircraft spotters during the war.

The advantages of the high aspect ratio elliptical blade were that it gave an ideal minimum induced drag and generated an elliptical load-grading curve. This meant that the blade was rid of eddy-making end-effects of high resistance at its tip. Furthermore, because of its high efficiency, the blade needed only to be of small dimensions and so of small wetted area and profile resistance. When the boat was clear of the water the tip of the blade would, owing to its long length, still be submerged. This feature, together with the aid of the forward mounted propulsion casing would ensure that directional control and straight-line stability be maintained.

Here again had been another example of Shaw's inherent insight and his casual way of directing my mind in the right direction. I found myself continually accepting these challenges of his, always so softly put. I found them no burden; on the contrary, they became a source of enjoyment to me.

Shaw had many habits and instincts which helped me as a designer. One of these was that he looked for the advantages rather than the disadvantages in a new idea. He could ignore, *pro tem*, a disadvantage and press on with a new thought to see where its path would lead. I have often reflected what a different attitude is adopted by officialdom in such instances. A committee has a nose for ferreting out snags and then cherishing them against progress. Was it not a fellow councillor and friend of George Bernard Shaw's, on the London County Council, who, hauled before his backward-gazing, snag-loving, experience-dominated associates for an apology for having, in a moment of extreme exasperation, enlightened them on their lack of progressive outlook, said, "I sincerely apologize for calling you fools. I should have called you bloody fools."

Aircraftman Shaw could never be accused of living in the past. New ideas were welcomed by him and he would help to support, with carefully reasoned facts, those of them that he liked. Once satisfied with an innovation, action would come quickly, though quietly, to make effective use of it. I noticed that he tended to place great confidence in his hunches and believed, I am sure, that the supporting facts for those hunches would surface of their own accord when they felt like it, all in good time.

In arriving at the design for our propeller drive appendage, we went through a similar process to the one we had gone through in reasoning out our rudder blade design. Ridding ourselves of the usual tail shaft and brackets – always badly shaped and mounted for high speed in water – we invented a low-drag, engine-integrated, fully streamline, power transmission system. This unit, bolted directly to the engine's flywheel housing, was allowed to protrude through the planing surface and into the water, where it carried the propeller.

This new power-drive appendage gave us a minimum of wetted area and permitted a truly streamline section at all its horizontal planes. The end results of these design considerations were that, not only were we happily left with a minimum low-drag component, but, by virtue of its being installed under the boat's centre of gravity, we gained a streamline-shaped stabilizing fin a long way forward of the aft mounted rudder blade. We thus attained a perfect geometrical layout for turning and straight-line stability control.

This new power transmission forecast the future. In later years the principle has been used, with great success, in Sweden. The Swedish unit by Volvo-Penta that I have in mind is now sold all over the world and is standardized by many manufacturers.

Shaw, like G K Chesterton, was adept at turning a fact upside down in order to see what fell out of the pockets. A good example of this practical trait of his was demonstrated during our quest for still further reducing the drag of the drive appendage. Its frictional drag was governed substantially by the amount of engine torque it had to carry through its internal mechanism. This torque determined the size of the various bits of mechanism housed inside the appendage. The size of the internal mechanism in its turn decided the minimum size of the appendage casing surrounding it. The smaller the appendage, the less the drag as it was being pushed through the water; hence, the less horsepower and fuel required to push it.

I had pointed out to Shaw that I had got the drag figure as low as I possibly could. Without any hesitation, he asked me what would be the result if we installed two propellers on each drive appendage and rotated them in opposite directions at the highest practicable rpm.

I remembered that the Italian Macchi MC72 racing seaplane, built for the 1931 Schneider Trophy race, had tried the same sort of thing with success. This aircraft captured the world record at over 440 mph. The idea made sense to me and I wasn't one to hang back because of complications. The plan would split the torque between the two smaller propellers. The torque transmitted by the vertical drive shaft would be reduced because of its higher speed. Such modifications would shorten the appendage, narrow it and reduce the size of its lower, streamline extremity. The overall result would be one of appreciable benefit in drag reduction and propeller efficiency.

Another example of Shaw's youthful approach to a problem and the way he could, at the advanced age of forty-five, tear himself away from tradition, was his enthusiastic demand for extreme aerodynamic and hydrodynamic cleanliness. In 1933-1935, boats, cars, and aircraft, were shockingly untidy in their design and grooming. Shaw insisted on cleanliness of line above and below the waterline. This was not merely an attempt to reduce drag, but to make sure we reached the *ideal minimum* drag. The concept was a good one, for we were using the hull to do useful work both aerodynamically and hydrodynamically. At this stage in our talks the term *ideal minimum* cropped up again and again. We took it very seriously; it never became hackneyed. We uttered the words with reverence.

Shaw's idea of cleanliness went the limit. There was to be none of the usual excrescences for navigation lights, hatch covers, torpedo chutes, dinghy slings, armament platforms, winch gear, cleats and bollards, screens, water and windbreaks, water pick-ups, and any other gubbins conventionally hung around a ship like rocks on a shake roof. All such items were to be carried under the skin line and made extractable in operation only if absolutely necessary. All this was a full twenty-five years before even enlightened sports-racing car designers concentrated on cleanliness of line to any worthwhile degree. It is a hard thing to do, to do it well; and when it is done well, it looks easy. My contribution to Shaw's insistence on cleanliness was my professionalism. I gave him what he asked for in the most idealistic form I could imagine. I invented rather than designed.

Shaw's demand for high manoeuvrability and maximum possible acceleration and deceleration, triggered the basic idea for our method of launching the torpedoes from *Crusader*. The missiles were to be released from the underside of the craft, from behind the main planing surface, where there was an air gap between the boat's afterbottom and the wake surface left by the main plane. It would be like a fish laying its eggs. After the release, the craft would swing away, at high speed, from the torpedo's trajectory. This system was later patented.

With regards to planing surfaces I had, from the beginning, realized that no matter how beautiful to see, the lovely spray, picturesque bow wave and highly turbulent wake trough made and left by the speedboat in motion, indicated nothing less than

68

expensive energy gone to waste. This waste had to be paid for in performance and fuel. If all that lost energy could be contained and so conserved for its main purpose of lifting the boat, then the boat's performance would be increased considerably. With this in mind I had developed, in theory at least, over eight months, simpler and more efficient surfaces than the ones normally used in the industry. These new surfaces, together with the damped suspension system I evolved, would give us high lift, low drag, and soft ride. They would also give us, according to my theory, a negligible side spray and bow wave. The wake profile itself would be as clean as a whistle. This, if I could demonstrate my claims, would be "bit of all right". In fact, as was shown by later model (then full scale) tests, the wake was so clean in form, so spray free, and so mathematically predictable in its profile, that the prototype hull designs could be laid out on the drawing board with complete confidence, knowing that the resulting balance calculations would not be in error.

Shaw took a great liking to these new planing surfaces, but thought that immediately ahead of the spring portion we needed what he called a "wave splitter". He wondered if such a leading V-form could be geometrically determined to give a constant progressive slicing action through the water and so keep resistance and shock loading to an ideal minimum. This I managed to do without difficulty; and he was happy.

Late in our talks, I suggested to Shaw that it might be possible to develop a planing surface that would give an elliptical wetted surface at, say, cruising speed. With such a surface, even our inwash fins – shallow fins at the ends of the planing surface, put there to keep water from shirking its job of providing lift – could be done away with. The idea intrigued him because of its classical perfection. I solved the problem satisfactorily, but we decided to leave the application till a later date when a bigger boat than the *Crusader* was being contemplated.

Not until early 1938 did I again invest time in furthering the theory of the elliptical surface; then, having done so, I "applied for" a British patent in 1939. This patent was never filed for "completion", probably owing to a shortage of funds at the time. I have now no copy of its script, neither has the British patent office, nor have my

69

old patent agents, H.N. and W.S. Skerrett. The texts of provisional patent applications are, it seems, destroyed after a time if the full process is not completed. All that remains of my effort is an official patent application number (#9968/39 of March 30, 1939). I now wish that I had made a special effort to complete this elliptical planing surface application, if only for historical record. Perhaps, one day, from some dusty official (or private) file the long-lost paperwork will come to light. It will then be interesting to read it again in its original freshness and detail.

One afternoon, I was busily taking measurements in and around the bridge portion in one of Power Boat's triple-engined hulls, when Shaw jumped aboard and held one end of my steel tape while I took some key dimensions. I was then working on a request of Scotty's to design and develop an integrated, triple-engine, throttle control. As I worked, Shaw talked. He was in the mood for expounding some of his thoughts on future war at sea. I listened fascinated. I jotted down the readings from my tape as though I were on automatic. Shaw went from point to point, situation to situation, with the vivid descriptive vivacity of a Robert Louis Stevenson.

In the next war our new concept in ship design would give Britain a high-speed navy of superships, capable of tackling successfully almost every kind of sea duty imaginable. These ships would act not merely as pinpricking marauders and simple torpedo boats, as in the past, but as doomsday squadrons. It was the first time he had used the name *supership* and I liked it. The name excited my imagination. I stuck to it.

He emphasized that this new kind of naval force would continue to create havoc and nervousness, to sting, to loot and destroy; but, in addition to coastal annihilations, it would now be capable of fighting triumphantly in blue waters, seizing and occupying, while awaiting the main fighting forces. It would now fasten down bigger forces than in past conflicts, both on land and sea.

Shaw had convinced himself that by using our proposed high-speed, high-load-carrying ships, the centuries' old tactics of the land guerrilla leader could, when used at sea, be much widened and that the objectives of such tactics could be greatly expanded.

As in earlier times, a determined guerrilla band would rarely be defeated; but from now on it would be capable of capturing and holding special territories on a substantial scale. By using the capability of each craft to carry and quickly unload assault troops with their usual arms and ammunition, strategically important, large-area, landing sites and bridgeheads would be captured and held until heavier forces took over. During such assaults the landing troops would be amply shielded by the ships' intensive and accurate fire power from a wide variety of stably-mounted weapons used at comparatively close range.

He went on to describe guerrilla-type squadrons which would sack enemy coastal ports and towns, as and when desired, with complete surprise. He said such squadrons would be free from retribution by aircraft and land-based gunfire, owing to their great manoeuvrability. The hare, he said, was more adroit than the speedier greyhound, and our hare would not tire. He saw the tactics of our high-speed super-marauders in terms of dispersion and concentration.

As Shaw talked I became spellbound. I could feel the throb and roar of the massed engines as they raced to the attack, the sound of the pounding gunfire and the fierce drags and thrusts on the body as it tried to balance itself against the hull's tight swings and darts as it moved from defence to attack and back to defence.

When he had finished, I knew that what I was doing was important; that a high-speed navy was Britain's greatest safeguard for the future.

Before he climbed out of the boat he asked me if I really believed I had now beaten the square-cube law for good. I said NO, but that, between us, we had shortened the odds against it for years to come. I added, correctly as it turned out, that we had diddled it only until the next round. What I didn't know then was that the next round would be thought about often, sometimes agonizingly, but would not be won for almost another forty years.

As I walked back to my office, I knew that the supership was born. All we had to do was slap its backside and activate it.

Chapter 6: Hard Work – Splendid Progress – Tragedy

It was now 1934 and, after the theoretical investigation work and the sketch pad activity of the past months, it was high time to experiment with models. Then, if enough money could be found, build a full-scale test craft of practical size.

In a mood of restrained enthusiasm, Shaw suggested hopefully that after the model tests had been completed and finally analysed, we should design and build, as a full-scale test craft, a racing boat. He would act as test pilot. We reasoned that this would be a comparatively low-cost venture and that it would spectacularly demonstrate our ideas. I was delighted by his suggestion. Such a project was right up my alley. I couldn't wait.

I was aware that Shaw would be in his element putting such a craft through its paces. He was, without doubt, a speed addict. He enjoyed thundering along an open road. Neither rain nor high wind would deter him. To Shaw, speed was a poetic emotion. He told me one lunchtime, as we stood looking down at his motorcycle, "I have already put my madness into words. One day, perhaps, my spiel will be published."

We had no money. Any capital we could hope to come across would be minimal. We should almost certainly have to borrow against success; the amount would have to cover at least the cost of building the boat, the trials, the patent fees and much more. Shaw said he would estimate the "amount of boodle" the venture would take if I would look over his shoulder while he was doing it. But we never got around to this mediocre matter. On a later occasion he did mention, half apologetically, that when the time came he would make a "laughing guess" at the cost of it all. And, with that, I was highly satisfied and as glad to be rid of the boring matter as he was.

Shaw, who knew my birthday was on 24 May, said that we ought to name the racing boat *Empire Day*. I remember saying I felt as though I were to be decorated. He grinned and remarked, "Of course you are. And when the day comes, you must stick to the formal technique of acceptance and say that you couldn't have done it without the precious help of your second-hand drawing instruments, your company-snitched pencil, your Woolworth's exercise books and sundry help from an aged, yellow-gilled slide rule." I replied, "What about your own reward?" At this his only comment was, "I'm but the taskmaster with the lash."

Our first practical task was to attempt to prove our theories and general ideas. This could only be done by systematically testing each of the models I had drawn during my all-night travail a short time before. An experimental programme such as this would need expensive test equipment and accurate instrumentation. It seemed certain we would have to dodge these restrictions and that the artful dodging would be my affair.

I made a few small-scale models of *Crusader* and *Empire Day* in child's modelling-clay, only about six inches long; but they showed the hull lines fairly clearly in an understandable, solid form. They were of no use for test purposes but were excellent for blending checks and evaluations. Shaw asked me to photograph them which I did with an old borrowed, ¼ -plate, box type, reflex camera with a Zeiss Tessar lens and a roller blind shutter. Unwieldy though it was, it was a fine camera. I liked it and could have bought it for five pounds; but I didn't have the money.

I demonstrated to Shaw my proposed method of making the simpler test models – the ones without any fancy lines or double curvature in them. I used good quality thin white cardboard sheet. The sheet was easily and quickly marked out on the drawing board, then cut with my first aid kit scissors. The separate pieces were glued together and brushed with aircraft dope to tighten them up. Finally, they were given two coats of varnish for waterproofing. They were a good job when completed – taut and true.

I made a batch and tested them simply by pulling them along at the end of a string in the swimming bath at Southampton. Shaw watched and said little.

We were not seeking evaluation of the airlift phenomenon at this stage. More elaborate tests would be needed for that. We were feeling our way and expected merely to convince ourselves that we had a good general theory to work on when using our simplified forms of planing surfaces. We wished to see a simple, clean wake and we did. That, for the moment, was good enough.

I knew for a week beforehand that Wilf Pickerel was to visit the Midlands, so arranging my trip to the baths without suspicion was easy. Arnold Green had already left Power Boat and, though still resident in Hythe, he and I bumped into each other only infrequently. Just how much he knew about my affairs at this time, I am not sure. He might have had some suspicions because he talked to me many times about his own doings with Shaw – he knew him fairly well – and I had no inkling whether or not Shaw might have referred to me in any way.

These early models were tested for wake profile cleanliness and dynamic balance. Purely eyeballing them made our judgements. Though primitive in method, these tests gave us a practical start.

As the models were unusually light in weight they skimmed successfully at very low speeds and we were able to judge their characteristics easily. We learnt a lot in a short time.

Shaw took some of the strain by attending to the adjusting of the centre of gravity location of each hull. To do this he moved a brass nut along the top of the model being tested, holding it down with a piece of medical sticking plaster. This way we obtained the best planing angle for a clean wake.

When I arrived at my office on the Monday after making the first tests I found Shaw awaiting me. He said he had been doing some thinking over the weekend and now wondered if I could fashion a contemporary type, V-bottom hull, in the similar kind of lightweight construction that I had already used for the first batch of "Darwinian" models. Such a model, he thought, tested in a similar way, would give us a basic and direct comparison with each of the other models. By this simple comparison we would convince ourselves, without having to be Einsteins, of a genuine saving in energy when using our planing surfaces. After a couple of false starts I made the model he wanted. Its underwater sections turned out to be accurate enough for our purpose.

Not far from Power Boat's yard at Hythe, Vickers Supermarine kept a large but disused flying-boat maintenance facility on which was a fine slipway and a low jetty. It was quiet there and I knew the elderly caretaker.

On this slipway, one mid-morning, and with the caretaker's permission, Shaw and I eyeball-tested the contemporary type, V-bottom hull. The caretaker loaned me a boat-hook to which I attached the model by a 30-inch length of string. It cleaved its way through the rhythmic wavelets as they shot up the slipway. After my earlier quasi-athletic performance at Southampton baths, Shaw joked about this latest show of ingenuity by me and called it the "lazy man's way to a Nobel Prize". Joking apart, we were delighted to see that the wake and spray left by this model were far more pronounced and spread out than those shown by our own designs. They told us that, other things being equal, there was a greater energy loss with the contemporary form of craft than there was with our own.

During the test Shaw, that day resplendent in his RAF uniform, trying hard to keep it salt-water-spray and splash-free, had stood looking almost straight down at the model. He could see all that happened much better than I, being farther away from the water patterns being made. He kept pointing out the features of the wake: all rated badly compared with our own models' accomplishments. The comparison, he said, was "decisively in our favour".

Immediately after this test I listed the hull as number one in our model series. It became the basic hull with which we compared every other alternative in our Darwinian-triggered programme. We now had sixty-nine models in our series and that figure remained unchanged. I later replaced this often hard-worked cardboard model with one made from a solid block of wood, fitted with all the standard appendages made from brass and steel.

After the test we returned the boat-hook to the caretaker and he gave each of us a cup of tea. Shaw then hurried off without any more talk. A little later, after tidying myself up a bit, I got back to work just in time to go to lunch. My absence had gone unnoticed.

Primitive though they were, these tests were impressive; they did much to give us the assurance that we were not dreaming in vain. Later, more qualitative tests were to confirm our early observations; but at this stage we were content to strengthen our hunch that the step-by-step approach to the design of a super-ship, through the comparative testing of a well-thought-out range of models, was a sound one.

Shaw remained the final overseer. I listened attentively to what he said; but in the matters of day-to-day design and investigation procedure he left everything to me.

I believe that, at bottom, he was keen to bring our work into the open but did not wish to risk doing so until he was as certain as he could be that our claims could be proven and demonstrated successfully. He made many statements, here and there, hinting there was something new in the offing. But that was as far as he went. To my knowledge, no one ever took him up on these rather lightly-given forecasts. As for me, for obvious reasons, I was as tight as a clam. The remaining and more sophisticated models were to be made later; the full test programme turned out to be an intermittent, lengthy, almost painful one.

It was still August and Shaw, with his usual habit of giving me something to think about, wondered aloud if I could invent a simple but proper method of testing our long line of models. His basic idea was to find a way to test our various hulls, and the theories behind them, by using his method of direct comparison with a contemporary hull. The one that I had made would represent the lower datum for all our expected improvements. In a rough sort of way this was what we had done when testing the first batch of models at Southampton baths and at the Supermarine slipway. The V-bottom, hard chine, displacement boat that we chose for our, as it were, research foundation stone was a single-engined British Power Boat hull. This choice served our purpose well. Throughout the research programme it made practical analysis simple, reliable and easy to see.

My next task was to find a way to test our models in a way that would suit our pocket books and us. I disliked the messy and cumbersome method of towing them in open water from a dinghy. The thought depressed me. It was so unclassical. I thought of curious spectators, awkward photography, poor instrumentation, bad weather, difficult and time-consuming procedures and a host of other inconveniences that would give me stomach ache. I racked my brains for a better solution, but none came. I gave up, feeling almost ill. Wilf Pickerill noticed my distress and asked me if I was pregnant.

Then, as so often happens, my demon gave me a leg up. As I awoke one morning I remembered that, as an apprentice at Jowett Cars, I had been in the engine test bay when one of the engines had suddenly stopped, un-according to plan. Being close to it, I got my feet and trousers dripping wet from water flung at me from the test rig's flywheel. This flywheel, used on our home-made dynamometers, was designed to take a Prony brake on its outside. On its inside it was cooled by water carried in the channelled rim. When the flywheel was revolving at a reasonable rpm., the rim retained its cooling water by centrifugal action, but when it stopped the water spilled out on to the floor. We lived constantly with a wet floor and duck-boarding in the test house at Jowett's.

This recollection of a half-comic incident from the past gave me the idea I needed. It was a simple one: construct a wheel like the Jowett Prony-brake flywheel, but larger in diameter and lighter in weight. This wheel, containing water inside its inner-rim channel and turned by a V-belt from an electric motor, would give us a fast-moving channel of water. With the wheel running in a vertical plane, I believed I could locally straighten out the curved flow of the stream at the bottom of the wheel and dangle the model in it from a balance carried just above the flow.

The idea promised simple convenience, inherent quietness, low cost to build and operate and, perhaps best of all, it could be hidden from the curious. It was, too, the cheapest possible way of getting a high-speed flow in a small space. At last I got excited.

With some joy I put the complete device on paper. I depicted the drag measuring device and the movable and variable lift weight. They looked good. I showed the sketches to Shaw in the *Lord Nelson* at Hythe, over a lemonade. I had been on my way home to dinner when I met him hurrying to catch the ferry to Southampton. He became so interested in the idea of a rotating test tank, however, that he stayed talking for almost twenty minutes, a long time for him. When I had explained the details his first remark was, "Spurr, this is great! It's classical!" He made no attempt to add or subtract from the scheme.

It was in this month, August, that I heard Shaw hint to a visiting RAF officer, "We are on the edge of a great development in shipbuilding". I am sure he was thinking of *Crusader's* final design layout and, maybe, of the breakthrough I had made in the water channel technique.

Shaw was busy making improvements and additions to his cottage at Clouds Hill at this time. He told me a friend was giving him a hand. Just what they were doing, I'm not sure, but plumbing was mentioned. I loaned him a motorcycle chain wrench that I had been carrying around for years, and a few other small items that might be useful. I rolled up the stuff in a newspaper and he put the package in his pannier bag on the Brough. I also gave him a wooden gramophone needle I had made from dowel rod, carefully and quickly hardened in the blue flame of a match. On a hunch, I had rubbed its tip in fluorspar. A week later he told me the needle had performed excellently and that it was the best one he had tried up to that time. He then mentioned that he would be leaving for Plymouth for a while.

As far as I was concerned, our ship research had now become my only completely satisfying activity. I began to consider the idea of giving up my job with Scott-Paine in order to devote myself full-time to it. I could then work from morning till night on all that had yet to be done. There were many models still to be made; the rotary tank to be built; the sixty-nine models to be fully tested; the tests to be analysed and tabulated; the drafting of design proposals for a full range of advanced civil and defence service craft; the search for a sponsor for an early full-scale experimental craft; and much, much more. I knew I was being irresponsibly ambitious, but I had the powerful urge to rid myself, for good or ill, of my job shackles.

I knew that little more could be done at Hythe without working more openly and that suspicions would be confirmed. I would not be allowed to serve two masters. Again, I did not wish to make trouble for Shaw. Until I had thought the plan through for myself, I decided to say nothing to him of what was in my mind. There was no doubt that I was suffering from what Lord Nelson called *divine discontent*.

Rumours were beginning to surface more openly, especially among the higher echelon at the yard. I never found out where or how they started, but each was similar in content: Shaw, me, and a boat. Wilf Pickerill and Arnold Green knew I was fiddling with a superboat design of some kind but, I feel sure, knew little of Shaw's real influence. However, it was all getting too distracting for me. More and more I was being driven toward making a decision to leave Hythe.

Then, a strange incident happened that still leaves me wondering. One afternoon, in the middle of my dilemma, Shaw stepped quietly into my office and said, somewhat ominously I thought, "Scotty wants to see you!" He said nothing more. I remember three things very clearly: He seemed quieter than usual; he was looking smart in his uniform; and he stepped aside to allow me through the door. As I passed him I said, "Oh, I think I'm big enough for that." I don't know myself what I meant by that remark. Shaw followed me down the stairs, then disappeared.

For forty-eight years I have tried to recall what went on at that meeting between Scotty and me. Was there a direct confrontation between us; was Shaw involved; did the result of this interview quicken my decision to leave Hythe? A few days later I suddenly decided to leave Power Boat and Hythe. I estimated that I could live without salary for a few months, and in that time, I thought, I could advance the project to a higher plateau from which practical development could spring.

At this time I noticed that Shaw was showing distinct signs of concern regarding his forthcoming retirement from the R.A.F. I began to speculate that once he had left the service, and Hythe in particular, his interest in boats might wane. Unlike me, he did not have a mind that peered in one direction.

I realized the break would be difficult for him after spending so many years in the Service. I was careful never to bring up the topic for fear of depressing him. Whenever he mentioned retirement, I did little more than listen. From what he said on these occasions, I gathered that he would like nothing more than a job with little responsibility that could pay his rent and board. Not wanting responsibility became almost an obsession with him. I was a bit like it myself. He wanted to write but was vague about a definite project. To me he seemed apprehensive and indecisive, as though awaiting an inspiration.

As for my own predicament, I reasoned that by giving up my job with Scotty, going back home to Bradford, and sponging on my parents, I could last out for three months if I was careful with my meagre savings. So, the decision already made, I wasted no time in putting it into effect. I had reached a point in my work at Power Boat where I could back out without hurting the company in any way.

I told Scotty, Shaw, Pickerill and Green of my decision. Green, although he had left the company months before, was still living in Hythe. I felt close enough to him to let him know what I was doing. I'm sure that, at that moment, he grasped more of the significance of what I was then up to. All were surprised, though none said, "Don't be a fool." Shaw thought it a good idea, even a courageous one; and said that he too would not be remaining in Hythe much longer. He said it was quite possible he would be sent to the Yorkshire coast for a time and that, if that came about, he would visit me at Bradford on his motorbike. He said he had a good number of acquaintances and friends in Yorkshire; it would be no hardship for him to make a circular tour on his Brough and so visit all of us. A few weeks later he was indeed transferred to Bridlington on Yorkshire's east coast, not too far from my home town. In the event he was without transport and so was I. He never visited me and I didn't get to Bridlington.

I left Hythe at the end of September or the beginning of October. Wilf Pickerill helped me to the railway station at Southampton with my bags and baggage. I was a little worried, as Wilf was suffering from a neglected hernia and I had visions of him collapsing *en route*. He was adamant about helping me, so I made sure that, although he carried the largest trunk, it was the lightest in weight. Unknown to him, it contained the cardboard models of which he knew so little.

Years later I discovered that Wilf and Arnold Green were brothers-in-law. This came as a great surprise to me, but I should have guessed it. The reason for the secrecy baffles me. So after many years, Wilf and I were quits. I had been reticent about my association with Shaw and he about his relationship with Green. I

80

had what I thought were good reasons for my secrecy; and, I suppose, Wilf had his. What an odd pair of close friends!

During the ten weeks that I was able to last out at Bradford, I did not leave the house more than a dozen times. I visited few friends or relatives. Most of the departures made from my little back-room workshop were to the Peel Park swimming baths, where I eyeball-tested the remaining cardboard models and new plywood ones made at Bradford Moor.

I tried to get to the bath early in the morning which I found to be quiet. On two occasions I arrived late in the afternoon to find the bath crowded and noisy. Luckily, the youngsters and some grown-ups cooperated sympathetically, allowing me to chase up and down the bath's edge without interference every time I needed to do so.

During this sojourn at Bradford, I laid out *Empire Day* and *Crusader* to scale for the first time. They looked good. Each drawing carried a full set of lines. It was from these drawings that the final display models were built. The drawings were used constantly for two-and-a-half years for reference work of all kinds and for "template lifting". They became the holy gospel and practical record of our whole work.

After the cardboard test models made at Hythe came the Bradford Moor group of models, made of half-millimetre thick aircraft plywood. These models were made in exactly the same way as the cardboard ones. Once more, the construction quality of the finished models was good. They had the advantage that I could attach metal fittings to them, which represented the necessary appendages. They were better able to withstand the inevitable knocking about they received in transport and rough storage.

In March 1935 came the professionally-made solid, display models used for final appearance checks, complete aerodynamic tests and, much later still, for special display before private and governmental boards. These models were attractively executed and were almost exactly as forecast by the rough sketches I had made for Shaw after our walk along the slipway at Hythe.

Three months later came the Feltham group of solid, wooden test models. It was the final and most important one. This group and the plywood group were never seen by Shaw as solid hardware. The

Feltham group demonstrated clearly, *multum in parvo*, our Darwinian approach to fast ship design. The group began with the contemporary V-bottom hull and continued through the main Darwinian mutations to our supership.

Although these models are long lost or destroyed, some of their photographs survive; looking at these, the steady, step-by-step evolution can easily be seen. This Feltham group was constructed and used solely for the hydrodynamic part of the underwater-section research.

The main aerodynamic investigation for determining ground effect usefulness and total aerodynamic drag, were carried out simply and quickly in the Von Asboth tunnel (mentioned later) on two of the cardboard models, one of the plywood models and both display models.

Altogether, from August 1934 to September 1937, I made or had made for me thirty-three basic test models and two display models, each one exactly as sketched and listed by Shaw and me at Hythe. Many of these were modified in accordance with our predetermined programme, so that they finally represented the sixty-nine different models in our scale of evolution. They were made and tested over a long period of time. The more important tests were accomplished mainly in the spring and early summer of 1937. The aerodynamic tests took place earlier in late May and early June of 1936.

Other models were made for the test purposes but these were not hull forms, they were components of all kinds, such as rudder blades, water scoops, propeller drive appendages, and interference fairings.

From time to time many of the solid-type test models were fitted with different kinds of underwater gear for comparative evaluation. Longitudinal deck runners were fitted to them to take the sliding balance weights. These weights were used for the easy modification of the centre of gravity location and for the alteration of a hull's athwartship polar moment of inertia. This latter feature was accomplished by splitting the balance weight into two equal parts. Each of these parts could be slid athwartships, inward or outward, on a crosstree - much like the weighted balance pole used by a tight rope walker. Underwater appendages, tested separately, were usually compared with a flat plate model of identical frontal projection.

Shaw's idea of simple, direct comparison of model performances, together with our enlightened use of existing aerodynamic theory as an analogical aid to the understanding of a high-speed boat's hydrodynamics, were of incredible benefit to me, whose talents worked best when using them for direct observation. The behaviour of water in motion is a phenomenon that can actually be seen and so, with a little gumption, can be fairly easily understood. It is the relevant mathematics needed to describe each phenomenon that burdens the dunce. Through Shaw's insight and my perseverance, the more difficult mathematics was artfully dodged.

I wrote to Shaw from Bradford, hinting that he should pay me a visit. I told him I had much of interest to show him. He replied, "I'm here till Feb. 28 but tied by the leg. I have no motor-bike here, and no time to use it if I had. The ten RAF boats (five cruisers and five armoureds) are in a garage in the town, under refit, with myself to watch points for Air Ministry."

Disappointed to hear that he was so busy, I was appeased when he said, "You'll be glad to hear that your big gear box did admirably as linked to the Gardner light-fast Diesel. We ran it for 50 hours off Hythe without an adjustment. It is the softest and juiciest clutch I've ever felt." This pleased me immensely. I had spent a great deal of my time at Hythe designing and engineering this unit from scratch. Our chief mechanic, Munro, had assembled it while Shaw and I looked over his shoulder. Leaving the yard, I had missed its ocean test programme conducted by Shaw.

This forward-and-reverse gear box was intended for direct integration with the 500 h.p. Napier *Lion* aero-marine engine; but as Shaw mentioned in his letter, the initial tests were made with the unit attached to the Gardner Diesel.

My modest resources ran out after ten weeks in Bradford. During that time I saw that I must get some experience in all-metal flying boat design. So I pawned my solid-gold, half-hunter pocket

Ozone Hotel
Bridlington
Yorks.
31 · 1 · 35

Dear Spurr

I lost your letter — or rather, I sent it to my cottage and so had no note of your address. Nor had Green, whom I saw in Bridlington a month ago! A bright pair.

Your letter interested me. I feel that engines — petrol engines — are at very nearly their best: that hulls are only in their beginnings, and propellors hardly even that. There is plenty of room for research, indeed!

Our 37½ foot boats are about as far as planing displacement hulls have yet gone: that is, they are a pretty level compromise between speed, cost and seaworthiness. Twenty years hence, I hope, something very different will rule.

I'm here till Feb. 28, but tied by the leg. I have no motor-bike here, and no time to use it, if I had. The ten R.A.F. boats (five cruisers and five armoured) are in a garage in the town, under refit, with myself to watch points for Air Ministry.

You'll be glad to hear that your big gear box did admirably as linked to the Gardner light fast Diesel. We ran it for 50 hours off Hythe without an adjustment. It is the softest and juiciest clutch I've ever felt.

After February the R.A.F. discharge me, and thereafter I've got to look after myself: not immediately, for I have enough for at least six months, but as soon as is convenient. I have not an idea in my head: various jobs have been offered, but none of them attractive. Possibly I shall fall back on my cottage and see how much — or rather how little — I really need.

I hope your plans are satisfactory to yourself. Research is a sport, rather than a living: but you may be fortunate in getting something jog-trotty at Bradford to keep you in comfort while you do your thinking.

Green was not too wise: he tried to persuade Whites, of Cowes, to build an almost facsimile Power boat: they committed themselves some of the way, till the question of proprietary designs came up: and then there was an almighty row behind the scenes. I'm out of it now; but I fancy Scotty strengthened his position, on the whole. You are well away!

Yours
T E Shaw

A letter sent by Shaw in Bridlington to Spurr in Bradford

watch (a prize for race walking) to put money in my purse and I joined the design staff of Saunders-Roe, flying boat manufactures, at East Cowes, in the Isle of Wight.

I took a minor post in order that I could still keep up my thinking. Cowes put me geographically close to Southampton, within striking distance of Shaw's cottage in Dorset. He was to live there when he retired from the RAF; and that time was almost upon him. All fitted in neatly and tidily; future prospects for the supership looked good. Although Shaw and I would not be working under one roof, as we were at Power Boat, I figured that we could meet, once in a while, in Southampton. I felt that our work could continue without much real inconvenience for either of us.

In early February, 1935, I remember writing to Shaw from East Cowes (he was still at Bridlington, in Yorkshire) telling him that I felt it was about time I made an effort to obtain a higher education, particularly in mathematics and English. I touched but lightly on our boat work. This letter turned out to be my last to him, one to which I received no written reply. I doubt that it required one.

Early in 1935, I came across two technical papers[2], which seemed to read so closely the minds of Shaw and myself that I can only look on the coincidence as one of subconscious mental telepathy and cooperation. I never cease to be awed by the astonishing fact that minds living many miles apart can think, not merely in parallel, but often in close and overlapping detail. It is a remarkable phenomenon which has happened to me more than once in my lifetime. It always amazes me, but I have come to expect it.

It was as though we had all worked together under the same roof. In most instances the mathematics of Perring, Johnston and Shoemaker, was more refined and academic than ours. On the other

---

[2] *Hydrodynamic Forces and Moments on a Simple Planing Surface,* Perring and Johnston, Feb.1935 Aeronautical Research committee, R and M No. 1646.

Shoemaker, Nov.1934 N.A.C.A. Technical Note 509. *Tank Tests of Flat and V-bottom Planing Surfaces,*

hand, our results were easier to follow and simpler to apply. Taken together, the combined efforts of the five of us to understand the fluid mechanics and to improve the performance of the high-speed boat's planing surface raised the study from an art to a science. We broke the back of the black-magic-guided dilettantism, which had ruled until then.

In February 1935, while still stationed at Bridlington, Shaw was retired from the RAF. He returned to his cottage in Dorset where he began to live on a pitifully small income, mainly, I believe, his pension from the RAF. He had already written to me saying that, "after February the RAF discharge me, and thenceforward I've got to look after myself: not immediately, for I have enough for at least six months, but as soon as is convenient, I have not an idea in my head: various jobs have been offered, but none of them attractive. Possibly I shall fall back on my cottage and see how much – or rather how little – I really need."

I was surprised at the time and am even more surprised today, to think that the British government could have been so addle-headed concerning its responsibility for the safety of the realm as to allow Shaw to retire at so young an age and so ignominiously. He could, I am sure, have been persuaded to become the country's first national director of high speed ship development – civil and defence. In such a post he would have been at his post-war best. Shaw's brilliance as a leader and mentor would have inspired perhaps one of the greatest research teams in British naval history. The complacent government, and the sleeping Admiralty, fumbled the pass; they missed the finest wing shot at goal in two generations. Sea power is as important today as ever it was – some experts and students, including myself, think even more so – but it must be the right kind of sea power.

In hindsight, I sometimes wonder why Shaw did not broach the subject and strength of our research to some high authority at Whitehall. With his retirement, he was free from any obligation or complication imposed on him by the RAF. I, on my part, had severed my connection with Power Boat. We were both free of our halters. Perhaps Shaw did, indeed, plant the seed, but with his death, the seed was left to perish. Be that as it may, it was I who became the sole guardian of his marine genius. I guarded it well and I tended it with solid endeavour.

Late one afternoon in early March, just after Shaw had retired, I met him at the left-luggage counter at Waterloo Station. I was weary and I think he was too. I showed him the two new display models by resting them on one end of the shiny, steel-covered, counter top. One model was of the racing boat *Empire Day*, the other of *Crusader*, the 100-ft., torsion bar suspended, motor torpedo boat. Earlier in the day I had carried them from Hendon where they had been made. They had cost me a fortune, a total of eighteen pounds, ten shillings. I was left broke. Both models looked first rate. Shaw's eyes shone with pleasure as he ran the tips of his fingers along the length of *Empire Day*. Then, as he looked up at me, he said very quietly, "You have an honest talent, Spurr. Cling to it."

We talked about the proposed armaments to be installed in *Crusader*; and about the possibility that Rolls-Royce might be induced to step up the power of the six engines we hoped to install in it.

He began to talk of big ships to be built on the lines of *Crusader*. I reminded him that we could not, as yet, risk going beyond a length of 150-ft. He looked at me questioningly, as though awaiting my confirmation that, with a little more effort, further cheating of the square-cube law might be accomplished. But I remained silent.

He then spoke of his retirement and told me it would take him months to get used to the idea that he was now on his own. He didn't seem happy.

Quietly and without fuss, he departed; and I was left wondering. He had been quieter, and more introverted than I had ever seen him. I sensed that his mind was on more immediate problems than those connected with the design of a high-speed ship of the future.

The design problems were now settled in theory, though not yet by fitting experiment; and I was beginning to look forward to further cooperation with Shaw during the making of the tests, especially now that he was retired and not too far distant from me. I never mentioned these thoughts of mine to him. I had seen that he was uncertain of himself at this time.

I received a short note from Shaw, just short of a page in length, during April. It said that he would give me a ring on the telephone one day soon, from Hythe. I recollect one comment he made. It was to the effect that "a boat at speed is a living thing, and at rest it is a soothing cradle in which to dream." He mentioned that he was overpowered by retirement, and was unable to fasten his mind on anything for long. This note was among the papers, referred to later, that were left in Durban, South Africa.

At the end of April, while at my work at Saunder's, I received a telephone call from Shaw. I took it on the open floor of the drawing office. He asked me what was "cooking", and how was the water wheel coming on? I said I was "fiddling about" doing some primitive tests on a wooden-made rudder blade, and that I had completed the working drawings for the making of the water wheel. He said how he had liked the display models. Returning to the rudder blade, he said he envied me my unimpaired passion for enquiry. He referred to the letter I had sent him while he was still in Bridlington and said that if I really wanted a degree in mathematics, why not attempt a University of London external degree. He said I could do it solely by correspondence. He said I did very well without one anyway, and that after all this was over I would get sick of being offered honorary degrees of all kinds. With this, I remarked that, although I was known as a mechanical engineer, I should like to go out finally as a naval architect, as it was in that capacity that I had indulged my greatest passion for research and innovation. All this was unusual talk; we had never discussed such things before.

Shaw knew Cowes well. He had been stationed there at one time. I was in the middle of suggesting a meeting at the Bell Inn, near the floating bridge on the Medina, the bridge between East and West Cowes, when we were abruptly cut off. Alas! I never heard his voice again.

On May 13, I was stunned when I heard over the wireless that T E Lawrence, Lawrence of Arabia, had been seriously injured in a road accident near his cottage in Dorset and that his life was in mortal danger. The details leading up to the accident have never been satisfactorily established. Less than a week later, on the following Sunday morning, he died, never having regained consciousness.

I made no attempt to attend the funeral. I was sad and discouraged; I had no wish to turn sadness into depression and discouragement into dejection.

In a lot of ways, all of them deep down, I never got over the death of Shaw.

Chapter 7: The Long Struggle Begins

Almost immediately after Shaw died, I left Cowes and settled in Feltham, Middlesex. I joined British Aircraft, at Hanworth Aerodrome, to be near the National Physical Laboratory at Teddington. It was a shot in the dark but I entertained hope of obtaining some kind of aid from that great institution. However, it soon became evident that I was just another pushing young man. I got past the front door fairly easily. I even had a job offered me at the William Froude Memorial Tank (at a comparatively low salary), but I couldn't find a way of promoting my own research. My simple machinations came to nothing.

It pleases me to remember that everyone at the NPL was very nice to me. The director himself showed me some of the research then in progress, including a paper he was writing. I noticed that it contained a lot of triple integrals and at least one mathematical sequence that frightened me almost to the point of paralysis. Eventually, he handed me over to a young man about my own age named Todd and this young man showed me the Tank and described its operation in clear detail.

It was at British Aircraft that I first met Bob Fields. We soon became good friends. He was in charge of our experimental shop and left his imprint on every item made in it. Bob had received a thorough and rigorous training as a cabinet-maker and piano-maker and, as our company specialized in wooden-built aircraft, Bob's practical skills became an invaluable part of the quality of our prototypes. These skills shone out from every structure he built with dazzling brilliance. I had never seen anything like it. The things he could do in wood I had never before thought possible. I didn't know it then but Bob Fields was to play the most important part in my life for more than two years. Without him I could have done little. He was a fine craftsman and a fine man.

While I was living in Feltham I got a number of the solid-type test models made for me by my landlady's son, a young man named Taylor. He was a joiner of some skill and charged me only five shillings for each model. In some cases I had three models made of each hull, each being a different size so that when I got my rotary tank finally built I would be able to compare scale effects by extrapolation.

In Feltham I purchased a Norton *International* motorcycle. I gave sixty pounds for it, slightly used. This model was considered the thoroughbred of thoroughbreds; its overhead camshaft engine would have delighted Shaw who could never resist the charms of a fast two-wheeler. Its mechanism was, for its period, the epitome of perfection and I was very proud of the machine's performance. I later fitted a super-sports sidecar to it as a family conveyance and fast cargo-lugger. It never let me down.

Edward Spurr on his beloved Willo'

My motorcycle became known among my friends as *Will-ó-the-Wisp or Willo'* for short. On one occasion I inadvertently outpaced a motorcycle policeman for over four miles before he caught me stationary at a traffic light. He charged me, reluctantly, for serenely passing through a red light as though I were in a Sunday parade; but he stood and admired *Willo'* for ten minutes afterwards. This happened on the Kingston bypass where, a couple of years later,

I used to 'drag' Fred Dixon in his Riley car, whenever I got a chance. Once only did he let me win.

I have by me, as I write, a news-cutting from a journal of that time. It puts me among the élite. Unbelievably, it reads, "It would be good for everyone, buyers and builders, were it possible to induce such men as Simpson, Scott-Paine, Cooper, Will-ó-the-Wisp Spurr, Ricardo and, say, Geoffrey de Havilland to pool their ideas and methods for one grand slam towards boat development and production." It surprises me more than ever when I read it now for, at that time, any fame I could claim was local and minimal.

Opportunity and luck did not desert me entirely. Through living in Feltham and knowing a friend George Stone, who had an incredibly successful habit of keeping his ear close to the ground and profiting from it, I was offered the chance of designing and engineering a three-foot, open jet, wind tunnel for Oscar von Asboth. I grasped this "break" with greedy eagerness and frenzied enthusiasm. A wind tunnel! Just what I needed!

Oscar von Asboth had recently arrived in London from the Berlin Laboratories. He was a casualty of the Hitler régime. Backed by the British government, he was in the process of establishing a small laboratory at Bloomsbury where he intended to continue his researches into the auto-rotation and lifting characteristics of helicopter rotor blades. As soon as possible we were to design and detail a helicopter which was to be built by the Blackburn Aeroplane Company in Yorkshire. A young scientist called Dr. Kraus and myself did much of the work although, as far as I was aware, the machine never reached the final assembly stage before the British government cut off its backing. The problems were not of a technical nature, but some kind of alleged mismanagement.

After I had designed and constructed the wind tunnel, I found myself in the aerodynamics' business at no cost to myself, in close and friendly touch with German experts whose brains I could pick. Dr. Kraus and I carefully checked the maximum air velocity at the open jet with the aid of a water-filled, glass U-tube. It was 40 feet per second and apparently quite adequate for them – and, I decided, for me!

During my last weeks at von Asboth's I made use of the tunnel whenever I got a quick opportunity to do so. I learned to make comparative tests in a few seconds with the aid of the simpler models and my cunning pendulum balance, mounted on an ever-ready piece of plywood. With my model of the moment already mounted on its working base, and with the pendulum already attached, it was ready to be clamped quickly to the bottom rim of the open jet grille.

It was in the Asboth tunnel, using these simple methods, born of Shaw's philosophy, that I further demonstrated to myself the inherent value of our air-lift form of hull. The results were close to the ones I had estimated and predicted for Shaw at Hythe. From this time forward I never lacked confidence in any air-lift computations that I had to make.

I first met Noel Pemberton-Billing in early 1936. Though I had known of him for many years I had never realized the brilliance of the facets that made up his character and reflected the unique quality of his work. By the May of that year, with the news not good at von Asboth's, I joined Pemberton-Billing at London Laboratories, in Sloane Square, as his chief engineer and designer. I missed the von Asboth tunnel although I suffered no hardship. By that time I had collected all the data I needed to complete my analysis of low-clearance ground effects. Not long after I left von Asboth, the Bloomsbury Laboratory was closed down.

Once again I was fortunate in my change. From the first, P-B treated me as though I were his son. We became close friends. On a number of occasions, when there was heavy thinking to be done and costly choices to be made, I stayed at his home in Shepperton. The laboratory itself was over the top of the Sloane Square Theatre. This theatre was leased to P-B and he used it as a cinema-repertory theatre. He screened older films of quality and made enough money from the venture to pay the running expenses of the laboratory. There was something left over which paid for extras of all kinds, including occasional pieces of new equipment for the lab.

After I had been with him at Sloane Square for about three months, he decided to move the laboratory to a place nearer his home. We found suitable premises at Kingston-on-Thames. I organized the new laboratory for him, bought additional equipment and engaged more staff. We continued our experimental work which embraced all kinds of projects: a camera; a helicopter (the Durotofin); a sixteen-cylinder swash-plate, aircraft engine (unique, in that it had four separate expansions per cylinder); a small, open fuselage, parcel-carrying aeroplane and a very complex game for teaching students of flying how to improve their total awareness against all flying hazards. Later, to my consternation, P-B became interested in developing an experimental, high speed boat of large displacement.

One day P-B's cook told me that the estate had "once belonged to Huxley, the monkey man". Perhaps that was true. Wherever one looked, on balustrades, on doorways, in cornices and on fireplaces, life-size monkeys were sculpted in every thinkable monkey pose. There were so many that I soon began not to notice them.

Sometimes if P-B were not feeling well, or I arrived early in the morning before he had arisen, I would sit near the foot of his bed on a bedroom stool and discuss his brainwaves of the previous night.

His room was in authentic Chinese décor; furniture, rugs, walls and ceiling. The lacquer work alone must have cost a fortune. The colours were magnificent, mainly blue and gold. The dining room was in pale yellow, including the carpet.

Once out of bed, P-B, who often slept naked, would put on his Chinese dressing gown, place his monocle in his eye, stride into the bathroom, drop the dressing gown, turn on the shower and keep on talking to me above the sound of the splashing water.

There was never a dull moment with P-B, nor an idle one. I enjoyed his company, his kindness, his humour and his fascinating stories from life – many about famous people. One interested me very much. It was about my old boss, Hubert Scott-Paine. I had known the story in part but, listening to P-B, I heard more of the details.

Sometime before the First War, P-B had come across Scotty, as a youngster, scrapping with his bigger brother outside their parents' hardware store at Shoreham-by-Sea. P-B admired the youngster's courage and, as soon as he had finished his schooling, gave him a job as chauffeur, secretary and general handyman. Scotty did his job well. When the First War came P-B opened a small experimental workshop for building seaplanes. It was nothing more than a hole in the wall with the chalked design of a seaplane on its floor. But P-B, who was a Member of Parliament, attempted to get contracts from the government. This action brought down on his head unbelievably heavy criticism from his fellow MPs. To avoid further bellyaching and accusations of conflict of interest P-B informed the house, with much show of autocratic pomp, "I will SELL my Supermarine factory." And he did, to Vickers, on the condition that they retained Hubert Scott-Paine and gave Scotty a goodly interest in the new Vickers Supermarine company at Southampton. Scotty himself sold his stock in Supermarine in 1925 and walked away with a small fortune. Sometime later, he formed the British Power Boat Company at Hythe and was its sole owner.

P-B had an electrically-powered canoe. When he became interested in developing a high-speed boat, we used it for towing models in the Thames which flowed past his home at the bottom of his garden. Whenever I found an opportunity to take out the canoe by myself, I would slip in a model of my own. This wasn't too difficult to do.

It was this gradually developing interest of his in the high-speed boat that finally made me decide to leave P-B. Holding back Shaw's and my findings from him had become too difficult. Once again I found myself playing a double game. This time I didn't enjoy it. I went through much mental anguish over this. I hadn't the heart to be secretive toward a man who was so kind to me. My instinct was to tell him all that I knew; yet I didn't want to do this. It would have weakened Shaw's and my effort for, by then, I was determined to make sure that Shaw got the credit he so richly deserved for his final effort on this earth to strengthen the country he so deeply and unselfishly loved, and for which he had suffered so much. I couldn't shake this altruistic compulsion from my mind. It was seated deeply.

I saw P-B on only a few occasions after I left him. The last time I visited him, just before the Second War ended, his health was beginning to fail. He was still working on a high-speed boat; he was still full of ideas for the future; and he was still as enthusiastic as the day I first met him ten years earlier. I shall always remember him as a brilliant inventor in his own right and a friend who was exciting to be with every minute of the day.

At the time of P-B's death, Hannen Swaffer wrote of him, "...once a member of Parliament, he had so many gifts – oratory, inventiveness, uncanny skill as a yachtsman, motorist and pioneer airman – but they were frittered away in law suits, fights and arguments. Otherwise as founder of the Vigilantes in the First World War, he might have been a super-Mosley. For he was Britain's first Fascist."

I can add that P-B wrote that true-to-life play *High Treason*; defended himself successfully before Mr. Justice Darlin, at the Old Bailey, on a criminal libel charge by Maude Allen, who was to act the part of Salome in the production of *Salome*. He invented and produced in Australia the first unbreakable gramophone record; and the superb *Compas* miniature camera was his brainchild. P-B was the first man to bomb the Germans on their own midden when he organized the successful British air attack on the Zeppelin sheds at Friedrichshaven, in the early months of the First War. In recognition of this brilliantly conceived and daring achievement his friends in the Royal Naval Air Service presented him with a magnificent jewelled insignia of the service. Ever afterward he wore this proudly instead of a necktie.

P-B paid me a great compliment when he told Sir Richard Cooper, then chairman of I.C.I., that I was the best listener he had ever known and that when, in due course, I decided in my wisdom to speak my one sentence, it would "contain enough uncluttered ingenuity to give twenty designers work for a month."

Noel Pemberton-Billing was a fine-looking man and, I would guess, six-foot-four in height. He wore light grey suits; white silk, hand-made shirts with extraordinary long points on the collars; no jewellery except the R.N.A.S. insignia; and a monocle on a long, black cord. He must have been about fifty-eight when I first met him, "Old enough", as he said to me, "to be your father." His hair was already silver-grey. His appearance was striking and dignified. He looked an aristocrat in every way. And he had a heart – a warm one.

With my friend George Stone of British Aircraft I joined Flight Lieutenant Comper at Comper Aircraft, whose offices were in the Strand in London. I had met Comper when he was director of Asboth Helicopters; we had got along very well together. We were designing a five-seater, high-wing, twin-engined, civil aircraft. I was in charge of the aerodynamics squad. The job lasted exactly three months then we were all thrown out of work. It was George Stone's fault. After our basic design was well-advanced, he told our financial backers that the machine "ought to be a low-wing job." The end came within an hour of George's pronouncement. Irresponsibly, we laughed, and prepared a stiff whisky for Comper.

Immediately after joining Comper, I had left Shepperton to return to Westminster. When the recession in Comper's and my fortune came, I decided to give up my idea of returning to a daily job with its restrictions on my activities. I turned a part of my Westminster flat, a large one in Belgrave Road (later to be bombed to the ground) into suitable working premises. I then set about my ever-present task of furthering the supership. Out on a limb, I decided to give myself a full six months to complete all the model tests and, faint hope though it seemed, arrange for the construction of a large prototype through the help of a generous backing from the Admiralty or from industry.

I had already begun to redraw the tattered and torn layout drawings of *Empire Day* and *Crusader*, so I at once completed them. I made no alterations of note; but this time around, I used a thick cartridge paper instead of tracing paper. One of them, *Crusader*, has remained in fair condition to the present day in spite of its foldings and travellings. The drawing of *Empire Day* was, I think, stolen from me some years ago, although a photograph of the drawing remains.

It was now April, 1937. My first self-imposed task was to build my water wheel. This I did and I sat it in the small, lock-up garage in Wilton Road where I kept *Willo'*. I gave the tank a high-sounding name, the Spurr-Westminster Rotary Tank, and took out a business name, International Research Laboratories, as an aid to obtaining trade discounts. All this bolstered my morale and sustained my ego as a businessman. I had some visiting cards printed, which made me look important as principal of the International Research Laboratories at Westminster. I tried hard to make up in ambition and showmanship all that I surely lacked in capital and influence.

The tank cost me about twenty-two pounds all told. Although it was not superbly constructed, it did its job well. I gave thirty shillings, a bargain, for its second-hand motor from a junk shop in Vauxhall Bridge Road. The wheel drum, supporting stand and flow straightener were fabricated by a small job-shop just off Belgrave Road. My improved pendulum balance was made as a "government job" at London Laboratories, sometime earlier; the special balance weights and lift weights were made by Wally Newman, also a government job, at London Laboratories. In the end I fared well. My only overhead expense was the three shillings a week I paid for the housing of the tank and *Willo'*.

I put the models through their tests. I took time off from the tank only to make the necessary model modifications and to work on the drawing board at my flat.

As each of the tests was made in exactly similar conditions, with the same equipment, the results were directly comparable, as Shaw had intended. With their completion, the tests at last gave me the full and sequential family analysis for which I had been so long, and so patiently, awaiting.

I wanted to sit down and quietly consider the progress Shaw and I had made. One thing stood out clearly: a rare feature of our work and one which was, I think, highly commendable for a complicated piece of research dealing with two different fluids in motion, was that our original theories and brainwaves had been accurate and true forecasts of the experimental results. There had not been a need to re-think any seriously proposed theory. Had we known it, much of the mathematical gymnastics and much of the model testing, could have been waived. The original calculations and sketch pad work, could have been fully accepted, almost from the beginning. The model tests confirmed the correctness of the original layouts of late 1934 and early 1935.

I began to apply for patents in November 1936. The process was a slow one. The first to be granted – and so published – in May,

99

1938, happened to be the first one that I had applied for (the basic, aerofoil-type of hull). Altogether, six patent applications were lodged and all were, in due course, granted. Also, two design registrations were obtained, one for *Crusader* and one for *Empire*

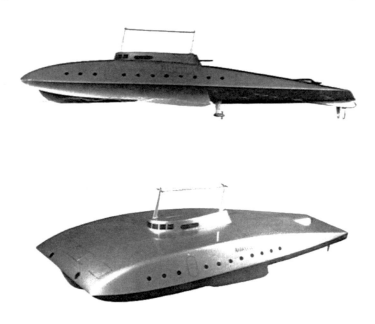

Crusader torpedo boat model

Note the aerofoil hull shape to provide lift and the streamlined bridge. All guns, bollards, etc., were to be retracted beneath flush panels when not in use, to keep the shape clean. The overall design is like Empire Day with the 'wave splitter', the 'inwash' fins and the propeller drives on legs. The twin rudders are elliptical in plan. What is not visible in these pictures is the step in the planing surface. Torpedoes were to be launched immediately behind the step into the air gap between the main and the stern planing surfaces – a patented design feature.

Day. A further patent application, the one for the elliptical-plan-form planing surface, was lodged in March 1939, but never got filed for completion. The time for the filing would have been early in 1940 and at that time we were fighting the Second War; so, times had changed. Also, my financial stability was weaker and more uncertain than ever.

Among the more serious tasks I was working at, toward the end of these free months in 1937, was the important one of trying to raise a substantial official backing for the development of *Crusader*, the 100-ft motor torpedo boat for the British navy. My efforts were futile. I could never engender even the slightest enthusiasm for the new craft, either at the Admiralty or in the shipbuilding industry. Many people, some of them important, some of them well known, were genuinely sympathetic but could do nothing to help me.

Apparently, this was not a time for presenting new-fangled ideas. I was amazed at both the official and the industry's reluctance to help, for it was plain to see that our future enemies were already baying at our front door.

I was keenly aware of what was going on in Europe. Shaw's wartime exploits had fed my imagination and aroused my interest in war studies. Even before his death I had taken to reading well-recommended books on the history of war and the First War. Later, in 1942, I furthered my interest by reading the subject for three years as an external student at the University of London. It became one of my preferred subjects at intermediate science.

My attempts to obtain worthwhile backing always resulted in disappointment. In June, 1937, I was asked to appear before an evaluation board at the Admiralty. On the appointed day I passed through that solemn portal with all due reverence, noting the statue of Lord Nelson in the entrance hall, thinking what a tiny fellow he was to have earned such glorious and heroic esteem. I was directed to a boardroom where the chairman, an elderly, high-ranking officer, was sitting at one end of a long conference table. I was placed at the other end with my notes, folders, display models and other paraphernalia set out in front of me. Seated down each side of the table were three or four other naval officers of various ages, ranks and skills. Altogether there must have been eight or ten of us.

101

After stating my case as best I could, I discovered that the chairman was as deaf as a door post and obviously undergoing great difficulty in following my discourse. The others appeared to be no more than curiously interested. A few polite questions were asked, but all in all, I made a poor impression. I gained a notion that I might have done a lot better had I been discussing battleships and cruisers instead of high-speed, hard-hitting mosquito craft – toys I think, to them. I sensed too that my unadorned delivery and Yorkshire accent cut no ice in such company.

I considered the meeting an official failure as well as a personal disappointment, although I came away from the Admiralty not completely disheartened for, as we passed into the corridor after the meeting, one of the youngest naval officers drew alongside me and, once out of general earshot, remarked, "Mr. Spurr, I think your concept is as good as anything we have had put before us. Try not to be disheartened. Keep pegging away!" As he turned away to re-join a companion, he looked over his shoulder at me and, in a low voice, declared, "Good luck to you." He was a nice young fellow.

It was by now obvious to me that there was but one course left to take if I wished to keep the work moving steadily forward. I decided to build the racing boat, just as Shaw had advocated in 1934. I would tackle it carefully and patiently in my own way; and, as best I could, I would finance it out of my earnings. I should not be able to build the boat to the original design of *Empire Day*, which had been laid out around a Rolls-Royce, R-type, racing engine, as used in the 1931 Schneider Trophy races off the Isle of Wight. I would have to build a smaller version, perhaps a one-and-a-half litre, supercharged engine of my own fabrication. When completed I should be in possession of a full-scale craft which could be used to demonstrate our new principles and their advantages before government and public alike. I could then hope that enough interest would be created to further my main plan of obtaining government support for the production of a prototype *Crusader*.

I delighted in telling myself that there were vast differences between the costs to be faced and the engineering facilities required, for the designing, building, and developing of a fully-armed 100-ft motor torpedo boat, and for those needed to put afloat and test a small, easily handled racing craft.

After making this decision, and while I busied myself with the layouts, assemblies, and detail drawings for a smaller edition of the originally proposed *Empire Day* in readiness for manufacture, I rounded up many of my friends and acquaintances in the engineering industry. I thought a few of them might be able to contribute help of some kind. Almost everyone I asked did so. There wasn't the slightest hesitation. It was unbelievable.

I lived as frugally as I could though, later on my health suffered for it. I learned that even a strong body can take only a fair amount of neglect without suffering distress.

During the time Fred Dixon used to visit me from his home in Reigate. I first met Fred after he passed through an unfortunate period in his life, long after he had become famous as a motorcycle rider, car-driver and expert engine tuner. As fellow Yorkshiremen we understood each other – he was originally from Middlesborough – and we became good friends. Fred gave me much valuable racing advice and taught me the wisdom of painstaking preparation. Before a race Fred could never be pushed; but during the race itself it was always a case of "the devil take the hindmost." He once told me, "Eddie, you can't win unless you're fast enough." He always emphasized that it was the little things that mattered. Years later I was reminded of this when I saw Maurice Chevalier in the film *Fanny*. Close to death, his friends around his bedside, he murmured, "It's the little things I'll miss – like lunch and dinner." Fred would have liked that.

When Fred Dixon knew for sure that I intended to build a small experimental racing boat, he generously offered to loan me one of his own un-supercharged racing car engines. But, idealist that I was, I told him of my keenness to build up a double overhead-camshaft, supercharged unit, using some existing parts from another engine as well as new special parts of my own.

Cecil Kimber, founder of M.G.'s (Morris Garages), told me I could borrow either an 1100cc unit or a 1500cc (neither was supercharged) and that whichever one I chose he would insure it for

103

me. This was kindness personified. Again, I told him of my intention to build up my own supercharged unit.

I would have saved myself much time, money and trouble if I had but accepted either Fred Dixon's or Cecil Kimber's generous offer.

In the case of Fred Dixon, when the time came, he played his part. When *Empire Day* was nearing completion he worked his wonders on my own power unit at the last minute. It was done calmly and unassumingly, in a poor light, late one Sunday evening in Slough.

By September 1937, not only had the tank tests been completed and analysed, the racing boat itself was completely designed and detailed. Little was left to chance. Many bits and pieces were beginning to be made. Such things as patterns for the foundry, a few castings, gears, new engine parts of my own, power-drive parts, rudder and operating system, special instruments, special maintenance equipment, and more, were all moving along nicely toward their delivery dates. But nothing of the hull construction proper was underway, except for streamline superstructure parts and cowlings which were being manufactured at Manchester by a young man named Kaye. He had quoted me a ridiculously low price for the work, yet he made a superb job of the parts. I hope I thanked him properly. His effort was a magnificent one.

I was in a quandary regarding the construction of the hull. It was not a boatbuilder's job and I could not afford the help of a fully-fledged aircraft company. Where could I find the expert group-skills needed for such work, and at low cost?

The answer came in November, 1937, when my friend Bob Fields, whom I had met at British Aircraft, came to my aid. British Aircraft had gone out of business and Bob had joined R. Malcolm, Ltd., of Slough. At that time Malcolm Ltd was a new, small company in the throes of establishing itself as a sheet-metal-working specialist serving the aircraft industry. The company was run by Ronnie Malcom and his partner Farquharson. Bob Fields held a responsible position on the works' staff.

Bob had heard from George Stone that I was working hard on "something to do with high speed boats." He rang me up and asked

104

me what it was all about. I told him, and of my predicament concerning the construction of the hull. I said how serious I was about making a success of it; that it was a commitment. Bob suggested that I consider the possibility of letting Ronnie Malcolm build the aluminium alloy hull on a cost-plus basis. He said that if I thought fit to talk to Ronnie, he would prepare the ground before my arrival. I jumped at the chance to, at least, talk about it.

A few days after discussing my plans in detail with Ronnie and his partner, it was all settled, easily and quickly. The arrangement offered me all that I was looking for and more: complete secrecy – the boat was to be built in a separate and securely-guarded workshop; reasonable, possibly low costs; aircraft skills of the highest order; Bob Fields' expert supervision at all times; and last, but very important to me, the comforting thought that I was among friends. So, finally, the die was cast. The hull was built at Slough and a fine job they made of it. Only Providence could have put in my path both Bob and Ronnie Malcolm together at that one particular hour in my life.

Bob was a Londoner, a cockney born and bred. His heart was kind and his humour quick. To him the countryside was a wilderness. The busy, noisy streets of London were his heaven. The metallic clatter of the swaying, bone-rattling tramcars, careering past his front door, were as Beethoven to his ears. Country life to Bob would have been as flat to his taste as unleavened bread. We became great friends; and, through him, I recovered my early love of tramcars (shades of No. 240 on the Undercliffe route!).

About two months before the hull construction began, and after having exhausted my six Elysian months of working full-time for myself, I reluctantly went back to the necessary but distasteful task of earning a living. In September I had joined the Chrysler-Dodge organization, at Kew Gardens, as chief designer, directly under the chief engineer George Dexter. I was thirty-one. During the twelve months I remained with the company, I was responsible for the design of five Dodge trucks from 30 cwt. to five tons, and a 26-seater bus. While at Chrysler-Dodge I still kept searching for major backing for *Crusader*; and I spent as much time as I could manage to pilfer from my daily job in keeping my eye on the

105

construction work going on at Slough. Toward the end of it all, I wasn't exactly sure whether I worked for Chrysler-Dodge or Malcolm Ltd. George Dexter was as adept as Lord Nelson at closing an eye when I needed to attend to my own business. Reggie Baines, the head of purchasing department at Chrysler-Dodge, delighted in acting as my buyer too. This way, once again, my own efforts and overheads were reduced beyond measure.

By March, 1938, *Empire Day* had taken on much of her shape. She looked sleek, strong and beautiful. But bills demanding payment were piling high in front of me. My earnings couldn't meet them. The long struggle became more and more a struggle for money. I felt glum and fearful.

Chapter 8: Lake Windermere – Frustration and Triumph

Let this small ship make real the dream it portrays, and so emblazon a bold and heroic path into naval history.
– Lord Strabolgi (ex-Commander Kenworthy), at the christening of *Empire Day*, 24 May 1938

To increase my liquidity I sold my friend *Willo'* to a dealer at Kingston-on-Thames for twenty-five pounds cash and a credit note for twenty pounds. This parting saddened me almost to the point of tears, but I bore up well when I remembered that with one more not-quite-so-tearing a wrench, the sale of my rotary tank for scrap, I would save the three shillings a week rent I paid for the garage in Wilton Road.

I got rid of almost everything I owned with which I could manage to do without. For the next two months I made use of buses, trains and occasional lifts from friends. Shank's pony, too, came in useful. None of these rearrangements made any real hardship and they were not for long.

To my heartfelt relief I was introduced by Reggie Baines to Norman Birkett – the foundryman, not the King's Counsel – of Stoke-on-Trent, who came to my rescue in time to prevent a complete collapse of our venture in June, 1938. Through Norman's generous patronage my financial troubles were alleviated for almost a year ahead. Norman was the kindest, most gentle man I ever met, and we became close friends.

Ten years later, I was hurriedly striding along a narrow trail on the South African high veldt, near Vanderbijl Park, when, unbelievably, I saw a figure I knew well about to cross it. The figure on the *bundu* was a long way ahead of me, but I knew that walk. It was Norman Birkett's! There wasn't a soul in sight, other than the two of us, as I ran toward him to grasp his outstretched hand. That evening we celebrated our reunion at the Riviera Hotel on the Vaal River at Vereeniging (where the Peace Treaty was signed which ended the Boer War), and to some tune. I was never to see Norman again.

In my quieter moments I can still miss Norman's beaming smile and merry twinkle in his eyes. He was a happy man, a simple man in all his tastes. He was courteous and unpretentious. Sometimes, after a couple of Scotches and milk, he would sing:

> You can't put your trash in our trash can,
> Our trash can, our trash can.
> You can't put your trash in our trash can,
> Our trash can's full.

He would say, "My mother likes me fat." He was my Mr. Pickwick, seventeen years older than I, though few would have guessed it. We laughed a lot. I remember him with sheer joy. Every minute I spent with him was a delight.

While the hull was being built I had the good fortune to come across a brand new 1927 Napier Schneider Trophy engine of 940 horsepower. Only a few of these costly power units had been built by Napier for the Supermarine S.5's and the Gloster IVB's racing seaplanes. John Cobb later obtained two of them which Reid Railton installed in Cobb's *Railton Special* car. In Cobb's hands this car gained the land-speed record on Bonneville Flats at almost 400 mph. This, to my mind, was a super performance for the piston-engine era of land speed record attempts.

The engine that I came across had, I suspected, been lost in the shuffle during the intervening years since the Schneider Trophy races. It was brand new. I picked it up without asking any questions for one hundred pounds, cash on the barrel head. It was the bargain of all time. Proudly, Bob Fields, "Kes" Kester (a workmate and a friend from Chrysler-Dodge, who was later to join us), and I, collected this fabulous 12-cylinder prize from Reigate where it had been quietly stored for years, and bore it triumphantly back to Slough in a borrowed pick-up truck.

I needed this engine for possible installation in the hull in the event that I should decide to make an attempt on the unlimited class water speed record, if all went well, in the summer of 1939. Should this come about, I intended to design for it our integrated, co-axial, propeller system, as originally proposed by Shaw. The unlimited class record stood at just over 130 mph and was held by Sir Malcolm Campbell in his first *Blue Bird* boat, the single-step hydroplane designed by Fred Cooper. I calculated that I could reach 150 mph or more using the Napier 940 horsepower engine. *Blue Bird* had used a 2000 horsepower Rolls Royce, R-type unit. A number of these R-type engines had been built for the 1929 Schneider Trophy races and further developed for the 1931 event. They had been installed in the Supermarine S.6's and S.6b's respectively. These were the racing seaplanes, so beautifully designed and built by Reg Mitchell, to which Shaw had referred when he compared their aerodynamic cleanliness with that of *Empire Day*.

About this time I met Amherst Villiers and his Italian wife at their apartment in Mayfair. He expressed a keen desire to see the new hull. Amherst Villiers was an old and valued friend of my earlier boss, Raymond Mays. They had been at Cambridge together. In his younger days as a supercharger expert he had done much to help Mays sustain his almost yearly habit of achieving *Fastest Time of the Day* at Shelsley Walsh speed hill climb.

I was delighted to show him the hull at Slough, although it was still in the unskinned stage of its construction. He seemed duly impressed but, a little while later, when he saw the Schneider Trophy engine lying in its cradle in a corner of the workshop, and was told that one day it might be installed in the small "flying wing" sitting on the trestles before him, he expressed concern. After a few detailed explanations and some sketching on the wall, he better understood our theories and agreed that I wouldn't, after all, kill myself. Not often, I think, is it easy to adjust to a radical thought; but Amherst Villiers needed little spoon-feeding.

The power plant that was to be used for the first trials of *Empire Day*, planned for the forthcoming August and September, was to be one of ninety cubic inches in capacity (one-and-a-half litres). It was to be built around a selection of Anzani engine parts which I had taken from the Eldridge Special racing car. This car was originally built to compete in the Indianapolis 500 and it had later obtained the world one-hour record at Montlhéry, in France. The engine parts had been very carefully examined and selected by me and then handed over, in an open wooden box – like so much scrap iron – to R R Jackson, the engine tuning wizard at Brooklands Track, Weybridge. He incorporated my own specially-designed and made parts and skilfully modified the existing clutch bellhousing to take the new, integrated power drive.

The unit was manufactured at Camden Town by a small engineering company, which I knew well, one that had made parts for me when I was with Asboth Helicopters and London Laboratories. The managing director, Mr. Davies, was a charming man. After each regular discussion at his factory we would adjourn to the local pub for a pint and a game of darts. When the time came for me to settle my account, he asked me to fix the charges myself and added, "Make them low!" Holding my breath, I suggested eighty pounds. Davies said, "Make it forty!" With a drink we called it a deal.

Jackson completed his work and the engine was assembled and ready for test. Norman and I went down to the track to see it perform at its first firing. It was music to our ears. The roar of the engine and the whine of the superchargers made the small building tremble. Its one hundred and sixty horsepower would not be rated highly today, but at that time it was considered very good. Unfortunately, we could not take as much power from the engine as we should have liked. Jackson had discovered definite traces of senile decay in some of the original light-alloy castings, particularly in the overhead camshaft casings. It was, however, a fine effort and we were pleased with the result.

The hull itself was completed in early May, more than two months before the engine was ready for installation; but we hurried along with the preparations for the christening ceremony. The engine could be installed later.

I was determined to capture the date of 24 May (Empire Day) for the ceremony; it seemed fitting and proper. The six patents I had begun to apply for during 1936 were expected to start coming through at any time. On 18 May, the first one did. So, we had kept our designs secret, particularly from foreign governments, until the last few days before disclosure of the completed experimental craft. Not bad timing for amateurs.

Through the help of Reggie Baine's brother, we were fortunate in persuading Lord Strabolgi to consent to performing the christening ceremony. We could not have done better. Lord Strabolgi, better known by some as Commander Kenworthy, was an ex-naval officer and an ex-member of Parliament before moving up to the House of Lords on the death of his father.

On Tuesday, 24 May 1938, Reggie Baines, Bob Fields and I took Lord Strabolgi to lunch at the best pub in Slough. For the occasion we had extended ourselves beyond our means and had engaged a private dining-room. It was a pleasant lunch for all of us. I remember telling Lord Strabolgi that I now felt I had reached the first significant plateau in my struggle to produce a supership of the future.

After lunch, we drove to Ronnie Malcolm's factory where Lord Strabolgi was to perform the ceremony. We had earlier dolled up the surroundings by placing a brown paper-covered dais in front of the bow of *Empire Day*. Over and high above the craft a large Union Jack was hanging. The champagne bottle was suspended in a string satchel, aircraft fashion, directly over the fragile streamline bow.

It was a great moment for me when, after I had introduced Lord Strabolgi to our guests and he had made an excellent speech, he struck the bottle a perfect blow with the presentation hammer and named the craft *Empire Day*.

As the bottle burst I thought of Shaw and how he liked lemonade; so I persuaded Lord Strabolgi to try once again, but with a bottle of lemonade instead of champagne. He did so and our five-year old dream materialized.

On the bow of *Empire Day*, inscribed immediately under its name in much smaller lettering, for all to see, though few fully to understand, was the simple statement: *To L. of A.: à compte* (To Lawrence of Arabia: in part payment).

Immediately after the ceremony, photographs of *Empire Day* were published in newspapers and magazines throughout the world; and our close secret, which had been kept for nearly five years, was disclosed at last. It was, at once, a relief and a new burden. From that day forward my life took a different turn. I was never again, for

111

one reason or another, to be entirely oblivious of my particular relationship with Shaw.

Surprisingly, not a single commentary that I can recollect mentioned any recognition of the true nature of *Empire Day*. Not a single correspondent of any of the major technical journals detected the new aim and purpose of its design. It was unbelievable. To experts and public alike it could have been a boat, a car or an aeroplane. One man, who saw it in transport to Lake Windermere, said he was absolutely certain it was a flying suicide-bomb; another thought it was a pocket submarine.

With regard to the boat's performance the experts were guarded. They preferred to wait and see. Some thought she would capsize; some thought I would kill myself, especially as I was able to climb into the craft only by removing the steering wheel and, once in, replace it and strap myself down inside the narrow, completely enclosed, cockpit. Should anything untoward happen, they said, then, "How in heaven's name are you going to get out in a hurry?"

I received much useful tuition of all kinds from men who knew what they were talking about. Pemberton-Billing advised me, and none knew better than he how to influence a board of directors along the path of one's own preference. He discussed the general tendencies and traits of the usual board members: the big investor, the small investor, the company accountant, the engineer, the easy-going dilettante, the chairman and the managing director.

During one of these sessions, P-B said, "Never, never, my boy, play around with the little man's money. He screams the loudest and the longest, and he might put you behind bars if you seriously inconvenience him." I have an idea that when he told me this, he was talking of his old associate, Horatio Bottomley, editor of *John Bull* for many years. Again, he told me, "Never laugh, never joke, never even smile, when discussing a loan or a financial backing. Money is a serious business, and you must look as though you can be trusted with your sponsor's worldly assets," and further, "Always talk profits and high gains, investors are greedy people." Like many before me, I discovered that there was, indeed, a working truth in much of his advice.

When I was asked to make a studio news-reel film for British Paramount at their London studio, Willesden, I was fortunate to receive guidance from Claude Rains' father. At that time I was still living in Westminster and Rains' father lived in the flat immediately above mine. Like his son he had spent his life in the profession. As he knew me well, he was kind enough to school me in the difficult art of reading my words yet making them seem to be extempore.

M. Rains took the rhetoric and starchiness out of the script I had written. He simplified and clarified almost every sentence and phrase. He then steered me into a semblance of a natural delivery, encouraging me to forget myself by looking directly at the camera lens and treating it as though it were an old school-friend.

On the day arranged, a Saturday, I spent eight hours in the studio, sweating and struggling to give them what was later shown on the cinema screen for only two minutes. I remember saying to the producer, when I was worn out and frustrated by it all, "Shirley Temple earned every penny she got."

In readiness for the arrival of the engine we concentrated on making many of the smaller components required to complete the power plant installation. There were engine controls; pipe work; engine mountings; a separate water pump for the cooling system and its drive from the engine; a hand starting system, its cowl; and many other engine-installation-related jobs to keep us busy.

The great day came in mid-July. We collected the engine from Jackson at Brooklands and got it over to Slough in unsuppressed excitement. Remember, we were all very young, and enthusiastic. Every day was wonderful: at this time, there were no blue Mondays. Every day was a Saturday or a holiday.

We fitted the engine in double-quick time. It dropped into its mountings "like a piece of egg" as Peter Berthon would have said. There she was: *Empire Day* in all her glory. Completed, she was beautiful to behold. In bright aluminium and royal blue, with the red, white and blue of the Union Jack emblazoned on the streamline bow and her sleek, almost exquisitely sculptured lines, she had a look of perfection. I could have kissed her. I had a feeling that Shaw was there, looking over my shoulder.

113

I decided in June that Lake Windermere would be ideal for *Empire Day*'s trials. It is ten-and-a-half -miles long and one-mile wide. In 1938 it still retained the measured-mile marking posts set up for Sir Henry Segrave nine years earlier, on its south-east bank, near Bowness. I knew the Lake and its surroundings from my hiking days. The memories I had were happy ones – from the beautiful swans of Windermere, my favourite hired canoe and the window in St. Martin's Church, Bowness, which bore the stars and stripes of the Washington family arms. On one visit I hiked around its banks and over to Wasdale, where, for a few days, I became a delighted guest of the Vicar of Wasdale. The rock-climbing vicar encouraged me every step of the way up the simplest climb – the *Rake's Progress*.

I arranged with Borwick's, a well-known yard at Bowness, to be there with *Empire Day* and my team mates by the middle of August. We used Borwick's because it was set on the Lake itself and was near to the *Old England Hotel* where Norman Birkett and I intended to stay. Borwick's was the yard used by the late Sir Henry Segrave at the time he lost his life in *Miss England II*, in 1930, after having already broken the then world record on a previous run. *Empire Day* used the same slipway that *Miss England II* had used eight years before; and the same measured mile off the south-east bank.

Owing to the disaster suffered by Segrave, Lake Windermere had not been used for high-speed record attempts in the intervening years. Segrave, it was said, had struck driftwood that had pierced the boat's bottom which was then torn away by the force of the water action. In spite of this we chose Lake Windermere because we liked it, knew it well and because we didn't believe the driftwood story.

We knew that Segrave's *Miss England II* had been fitted with a false step, attached immediately behind its original step, in order to improve its planing balance. This false step had been fixed to the boat's wooden bottom by simple coach bolts. We were informed, by witnesses, that the false step had worked loose on a number of occasions before the final catastrophe and that it had had to be tightened up each time Segrave made another run. On the fastest and fatal run, the false step had again worked loose and on that occasion, it had been torn completely away by the increased water forces of the yet higher speed attained.

The official members of our team were: Norman Birkett, the ever cheerful; Bob Fields, my indefatigable right-hand man and close friend; "Kes" Kester, truly a Rock of Gibraltar in any mechanical crises; Joe Lashmar, a friend from my days at Cowes and a first-class yard bo'sun; Reggie Baines, without whom everything would have stopped dead; Pete Lynn, who was on my design staff at Chrysler-Dodge, and one of the most conscientious fellows I have ever known; and Wally Newman, a good man with a camera and late of my design staff at London Laboratories. I brought up the rear as test pilot and general foreman. We were a motley company, completely unprofessional in our approach to all matters sailoring. But we considered ourselves good men and true for the purpose in hand. Shaw could not have asked for better.

Joe Lashmar was the only trained and accomplished yachtsman of the old school. He had sailed on King George V's *Britannia*. He had served his time as a boat-builder in Cowes and knew slow-speed water well enough to make himself a superb yard bo'sun. The rest of us were automobile engineers, aircraft men, designers, draughtsmen, and office workers. Our complete lack of reverence for tradition and terminology must have shocked the professional Lake-men and well-trained weekend sailors of Windermere. One example will highlight this serious defect of ours.

On 15 August, we lifted *Empire Day* by crane from the railway van, over and across the platform, directly down into the lake – her first ducking. We had to lower her many feet to reach the water. On the way down the after-end of the boat's streamline tail, constructed in wafer-thin aluminium sheet, began to swing slowly toward the rough, stone quayside wall. This was too much to bear for one of us. Without mentioning his name – we sailors must stick together – he yelled, "Slew the arse round!" Slowly, as directed, the after-end did as it was told and moved slowly away from the wall. We all breathed freely again.

Throughout the incident, the watching crowd preserved a stony silence; but I thought I heard a watching Shaw giggle.

To this day I seem fated to defy naval tradition. For example, I design a boat in the manner of an automobile engineer and draw it as though it were speeding across a drawing board from right to left. This is just another of those distressing instances when my instinct directs me and so keeps me permanently out-of-step with my compeers and age-old practices.

Once docked, we spent a few days making final adjustments, dock tests and safety checks of several kinds.

On open water our troubles began in earnest. Without greeting or formal introduction, Murphy and his law took over and we began to suffer failures and delays, which taxed our patience to the limit. Any other team would have jumped into the Lake and drowned itself. We, however, were different: we continued to work hard. After all, there was always dinner and a light ale to look forward to at eventide.

The hose-type water-pump drive from the engine failed many times, always at a critical moment. There were engine "flame outs", and starting difficulties, owing to water absorption problems connected with the special fuel chemistry. We had to stop to design, make, and fit water inhibitors in the fuel tank. The new, integrated power-drive to the propeller developed a hard, rough spot somewhere in its system. This fault was not remedied until after many inspections and dismantling, spread over three weeks.

We lost much time when a crack developed in the cylinder head. This was not an easy fault to put right in a double overhead-camshaft engine of small capacity. I got rid of this trouble by recollecting and the applying "a trick worth two" that I had learned at Jowett's in my early career. I rusted up the crack with a solution of water and sal-ammoniac. Although a *rodneyed*[3] job of the first order, it worked well when one considered the high combustion pressures of even a very modestly supercharged engine such as ours.

Propellers gave us the most trouble. This is not an unusual circumstance when attempting to reach a boat's peak efficiency. But in our case, in an attempt to save time, money and effort, I had made

---

[3] A Yorkshire mechanic's slang term meaning to fake a spoilt job well enough to fool a quality-inspector's gauge.

116

the hazardous decision to use standard catalogue-listed propellers. I bought these direct from the wholesaler's shelf. I then modified them to suit our special integrated power-drive by casting around the existing manganese-bronze centre boss of each propeller a larger one in aluminium. This larger boss was shaped so that its outer-surface faired into the power-drive's lower streamline gear-casing. The modification gave the whole of the lower end a perfectly streamline form.

Owing to this dreadful decision of mine the blades, in practice, suffered from vibration and distortion, then loss of pitch and sometimes loss of a blade itself. The problem was more than a nuisance; it was time consuming and, on occasions, frightening. It was not conducive to the pilot's peace of mind – my own – for him to be sitting with his backside just a few inches above the spinning tip of a high-speed, fluttering, knife-edged, propeller blade, which might be flung off at any second and pierce the boat's underskin (a skin that was only thirty-six thousandths of an inch thick).

Why, in Heaven's name, did I take such a slipshod design-chance when I knew the facts? Search me! I knew better than to do such a thing. I had done the one thing, more than any other that I can think of, that I would not have believed possible of myself. And what would Shaw have said? Had not my first talk with him dealt solely with such a problem? In that instance had I not, by inference, criticized some other designer – poor soul – for committing a similar error of judgement? Whenever I think of his blunder I hang my head in shame. Let me say though, in passing, that, in defence of my fellow designers if not of myself, the designer's lot is not always a joyous one; at times it can become the very deuce of a compromise, the compromise of the simple and the complicated, the cost and the quality, and, often, the old and the new. Lucky is the designer who is happy with his compromises! Sooner or later in his career, the practicing designer is bound to advocate a *boner*. When he does it will almost always show up at a critical moment. Such occasions are sobering and, as Pemberton-Billing used to say, "...will stop you from laughing in church."

Because of our propeller troubles we began to be dogged by clutch troubles. The clutch was a dry, multi-plate design (steel to bronze) and had been designed originally for the Indianapolis 500 car from which I took it in its entirety. It was not suitable for the kind of slippage I was now giving it as a result of our propeller difficulties. The plates began to distort owing to the extra frictional heat they were absorbing. We spent time we could not afford trying, not very successfully, to straighten out the warpages in the plates as often as they developed. Each time we had to do this the clutch bellhousing had to be completely detached from the engine, and the whole power drive lifted out of the boat. This manoeuvre took up much time and made incessant work for Kes. He never complained, although on one occasion he spun a clutch plate on each arm to the tune of *Colonel Bogey*.

Even when using some of these faulty propellers, I was able to get the craft on to the surface of the water and at speeds high enough to make judgements on her lower-range performance and general behavioural traits – before the propellers began to give trouble. On these occasions the craft rode excellently, felt stable, responded perfectly to the dagger-blade rudder and was free of hull panel-drumming. As a start it was heartening and gave me assurance of the kinds of results I could dare to expect during later high-speed trials.

Reporters and photographers behaved generously toward us. They were there in numbers and were very patient throughout our troubles. They gave us wide and lengthy coverage. I began to receive news cuttings from Australia, South Africa, the USA, India, Ceylon, New Zealand, Newfoundland, Canada, Rhodesia, the Malay States, France, Belgium, Ireland, Scotland, Wales and Holland. There were a few from places I had never heard of. Altogether I was sent over a thousand cuttings. And yet there was no serious response from any department of the British Government.

Every fellow in the press corps rooted for us and made us feel as though we could do no wrong. Perhaps it was that they guessed we were there at Windermere on a shoe-string. Many of them fetched and carried for us, as though they were inner members of our team and were as determined as we were to make the venture a success. If I had a single favourite among the pressmen it was J B Hardwick, a senior reporter from one of the Northern newspaper syndicates. He was older than I and his quiet efficiency and kindness got through to

118

me almost immediately after our arrival. Only once did I mildly criticize him. That was when he described me as a "modest Yorkshireman". I told him in confidence that he was mistaken: I was not modest but speechless from fatigue, anxiety and an active, burning stomach ulcer. We laughed and he was kind enough to keep to himself what I had told him.

In the two months before our sojourn at Windermere and during our five-weeks stay, many newsreel films were made of *Empire Day* and our day-to-day activities. Many were in the form of news items; some were made as short documentaries in which I discussed the more general features of the design. I recollect the lively activities of Pathé, and Gaumont-British, British Movietone, and Paramount, among others. For the good of our cause we did our best to cooperate. The days were hectic and the attention we got was flattering for all of us; but we found the notoriety a burden. We were not used to it, it was unsettling. However, we bore it all with fortitude and humour. As a result we made some good friends. I cannot speak highly enough of the press. They were great fellows. We had few secrets. I believe each pressman thoroughly enjoyed the simplicity of his assignment and, when at Windermere, the peace, quiet and beauty of the English Lake District.

Of course there were exaggerations in the coverage. It was said that Shaw and I had together made and tested over seventy miniature models of our craft (one report said as many as three hundred). This was not strictly true. Shaw had approved our Hythe, Darwinian-inspired, programme of sixty-nine models for test, but had only been directly concerned with the eyeball testing of the early, cardboard-made models.

Other press boners were made from time to time. It was said that I was a wealthy young man; that *Empire Day* had cost eight thousand pounds to build (a lot of money in those days. What it did cost, I don't know, but it wasn't anywhere near the figure quoted by the press); that I was a thirty-one-year-old engineering genius; that Shaw and I had worked for months making models with matchsticks and old metal; that Shaw and I found most of our inspiration in sleep at my lodgings; that Shaw had said, "If we had had these boats in the Great War, the Battle of Jutland would have been over in ten

119

minutes"; that I would challenge Gar Wood of America for the Harmsworth Trophy; and that I and a friend had "discovered a fuel mixture which may make all petrol fumes non-poisonous."

Because of the harassing problems and petty setbacks we were suffering at Windermere, together with the months of pressure preceding our visit, I was now beginning to feel the strain. Should work be going on that didn't need my attention, I learned to slip up to the loft at the yard and lie down for a while. In this way I kept my spirits up and borrowed time to think quietly. My ulcer was giving me much pain, I had often to visit the bog and retch. Bob knew what I was going through and kept silent; but he was worried about my worsening condition.

Our propeller troubles got worse and worse. In desperation Norman Birkett and I made a quick trip in his Rolls to nearby Lancaster and arranged for a special propeller to be made to my design in aluminium-bronze. I spared nothing in my generosity of blade overlap and large root radii. It was the antithesis of the *rodneyed* propellers I had been using until then.

We made the new pattern quickly by building up one of our existing propellers with clay to the new shape. Without delay we hurried it to Norman's foundry at Stoke-On-Trent and there had the casting poured immediately. The required machining and balancing could not be so quickly effected. Back in Lancaster I ended up machining its taper bore and end faces only, then cleaning up the blade faces and backs by hand. Finally being satisfied (for the sake of a quick test) with a static-balance check instead of a full dynamic one.

In this, virtually unfinished, condition we dashed back to Windermere and, not heeding its faults at this stage, installed the propeller on the drive shaft for a quick test. I intended to run it gently then try to reach medium speeds for closer checks before returning to Lancaster for final precision machining and balancing.

The tests proved unimpressive. The craft felt like a barge, and the transmission was as rough as the proverbial bear's bum. The thicker blade sections caused the sluggishness while the roughness due to the imperfect surface finish of the blades' faces directly affected the hydrodynamic balance of the propeller. These faults

120

could be expected at this stage of the propeller's evolution. But the temporary rough running *did* worry me. I was afraid that the transmission's mechanism would suffer.

While Norman and I had been chasing round the countryside, the team had taken the best one of our damaged propellers, cleaned it up and reset its blades to a fifteen per cent lower pitch. They said that with such a modification I should obtain greater flexibility of control necessary for our proposed rough-water test. This was a test I was looking forward to making, but it was one for which I had to await the appropriate weather conditions. The test would be a very important one. I thanked them for taking this initiative; it was a good idea.

That afternoon, while handling the new and stronger propeller I had designed, but had still to complete, I got a hunch to install the one the team had modified for me for the rough weather trials, get out on the lake and do my stuff.

It was getting late in the afternoon; the propeller had to be fitted and there were other needful preliminaries to attend to. But we made it, with daylight to spare.

Glory be! On the eighth day of September 1938, with a small bunch of forget-me-nots and a shining new penny in my breast pocket, the long-awaited triumph arrived. *Empire Day*, late on that dull day, in failing light, moved like the proverbial bomb across the surface of Lake Windermere, easily attaining her lower-limit, high-speed, design speed, which was faster than the existing world record in its class by over four miles an hour. It was so great a surprise, to me and to the team, that we had no time to treat the run as scientifically as we should have liked. We were caught totally unaware. It should be remembered that in those days, we worked and recorded mainly with stop watches, air speed indicators, slide rules, graph paper and note books – nothing was recorded automatically. I remember watching the air speed indicator and the engine's tachometer needle; noting that the ride was steady and dead level, there was no side spray and the hull felt close to being airborne. Control was light and extremely precise. Taking everything into account, *Empire Day* felt much like a superbly balanced flying-boat must feel just before take-off.

Empire Day on its record-breaking run, 8th September 1938. Note how little wake and spray she is making. You can see the exhaust smirch on the engine canopy and Spurr in the cockpit

Unforgivably, on the return run at an even higher speed, the propeller again distorted and failed. Owing to my elation, I looked on the failure as nothing more than a temporary setback. We could now concentrate upon the completion of our new, unfinished propeller and then press on to a praiseworthy final and official success.

That evening on the late BBC news from London, it was announced that *Empire Day* had unofficially broken the world record in the 400kg Class with a speed of seventy-three miles an hour. The existing official record, held by Italy, was sixty-nine miles an hour. I was pleased with our speed, and the even faster one at the beginning of the return run. I now knew that when our latest propeller was completely machined, polished and dynamically balanced, our higher-limit design speed of eighty-five miles-an-hour would be reached fairly comfortably. With such a performance I felt we should be much nearer to success than we had ever been in our quest of official sponsorship for a British navy of superships.

Crew after the record run, left to right, Wally Newman, Bob Fields, Edward Spurr, Borwick's man, Joe Lashmar and Kes Kester.

By good fortune a lone photographer obtained a good picture of *Empire Day* in the middle of her record-breaking run. This photograph shows clearly the kind of wake that we had predicted four years earlier and the beautiful balance of the boat at high speed.

Our success came hard, but at this moment we were overwhelmed with joy, grateful to the gods for their kindness. I sent a telegram of elation to my wife Edwina and young son John at Shoreham-by-Sea, where they were staying while I was at Windermere.

That evening we all drank a well-earned toast at the *Old England*.

Our triumph, however, was fleeting. Delight soon turned to frustration and bitter disappointment when, on the following morning, we found the beginnings of a fracture along a portion of the propeller's vertical drive shaft. In all likelihood this originated from the rough treatment the shaft had undergone during the lengthy period before we had determined the cause of its earlier course running. The added vibration loads imposed by the unfinished propeller had then, I believe, increased the damage further. This fracture was easily visible to the naked eye. It was a depressing sight to all of us.

As if this was not enough, we were struck a further blow when Kes noticed a hair-line fracture in one of the fast-running, supercharger-drive, helical gears. My immediate exclamation was the Yorkshireman's traditional one of "damn and blast it!"

Our optimism of the previous day now ebbed visibly. The two unwelcome discoveries seemed to sound the knell of a dying effort. Yet I found it difficult to accept such a petering-out kind of defeat so, in the cold light of an early morning discussion, we decided to risk the attempt of a further high-speed run to gather as much general data as we could. I knew the odds for success were poor, but after almost four weeks at Windermere our expenses were approaching what were, for me, the giddy heights of the national debt. Results must be obtained quickly. It had to be all or nothing. Now or never!

We had to wait for days before the complete transmission was reassembled and installed in the craft and for our new propeller to be considerably improved in finish. And there were many checks and adjustments to be made. By the late afternoon of 15 September, we were ready to attempt a sensibly-controlled final effort.

After warming up the engine and changing from soft spark plugs to the hard ones necessary for attaining full power, I took off. For more than five hundred yards I coaxed *Empire Day* along gently and gingerly. Then, gradually opening up the power and ignoring noticeable propeller vibration, I got her moving like a thoroughbred. Just as I reached this stage of the run, nearing the first mile-post, I began to feel uncomfortably hot inside the enclosed cockpit. I looked down at my feet and was alarmed to see the bulkhead was on fire!

Instantly, I pulled back the throttle control; pushed the relay lever of the fire extinguisher; jerked the release pin from my body harness; freed the windscreen canopy; dragged the steering wheel from its column and, with the agility born of obstacle racing as a schoolboy, scrambled out into the fresh air.

In the *Old England*, about an hour later, I was fully recovered although, I was told, excitably talkative and too laughingly optimistic after such a calamitous setback.

Empire Day looked a sorry mess the next day. We saw that, although she had not capsized and sunk, she had been badly damaged amidships. The all-welded steel bottom had kept her afloat and the broad bow had brought her safely to a stop without capsizing.

I did the only thing I *could* do. I decided, quick and lively, to call the venture off. We left Windermere swiftly, almost with our tail between our legs and we were glad to get back to Slough, out of the limelight, where we could once again continue our experimental work in peace and quiet and under less pressure.

Windermere had been a great, though sobering, experience. From that time forward it was to be wilful determination rather than high-spirited enthusiasm that kept us pressing on. Our cheerful bravado was gone; we were tired and stale – but much more seasoned.

At this point in our struggle there were many consolations for which to be thankful. Of these, the two uppermost in my mind were the feeling that I had done my best, in difficult circumstances, to keep what I considered to be my solemn commitment to Shaw; and the solid conviction that the design of *Empire Day* was, indeed, a truly advanced one that could be furthered with confidence if we could obtain adequate technical and financial support.

Only the Devil himself could stop us now.

Chapter 9: The End of a Dream

Before leaving Slough for Windermere we rented a small, newly-built factory in Ipswich Road, on the Slough Trading Estate. On our return, we fitted up the building with an office, store room, and screened entrance and we collected the essential tools and equipment needed for our continued experimental and development work. Bob and Kes made the alterations and additions. When they were completed the place looked trim and efficient. With its all-white paintwork and floor lines, it gave a hospital-like effect which appealed strongly to my inner need for complete mental detachment while doing my thinking and experimenting. It was the type of layout to which I had grown accustomed at Hythe. We were all pleased with our new home. We called it the Spurr Boat Company and, though our means were small, our plans and hopes for the future were high.

I had one regret: that I had rid myself of my rotary test tank. We now had ample space for it. I could have spent a fair amount of time refining its design and improving its operating procedure. With its aids, our elliptical planing surface could have been further investigated and I could have attempted to combine it with a small, open jet, wind tunnel for complete environmental tests. I tried to find the tank, but the merchant to whom I had sold it had sold his business to somebody else. The new owner, after a paper search, could not find an individual bill of sale and concluded that my piece of classical test-hardware had left the yard as part of a scrap metal load, sold by weight alone.

I now resigned from my job at Chrysler-Dodge and so did Kes Kester. Kes had been in charge of our experimental shop under George Dexter.

Then Bob Fields left Malcolm Ltd. A few weeks after that Peter Lynn (who by then was at Short's, the flying-boat manufacturers at Rochester) joined us as designer-draughtsman. From that time we each worked for a pittance at the Spurr Boat Company. In compensation for our low salaries we gained a daily freedom and satisfaction that was rarely achieved in an ordinary job.

No discipline was necessary or considered. We didn't punch a clock. Although I set and reset our programme, each man was his own boss. We never had a wrong word one to another and never lost our sense of humour, even in times of stress.

Our main worry, always, was shortage of capital; but Norman Birkitt delighted in keeping us afloat. There were no luxuries in our life and the wolf never wandered far from our door. We told one another that all this was character-forming; and with such a pious belief we contented ourselves. We were sure that, in the end, our perseverance would be rewarded.

The state of my health was still causing me difficulty, but there was no respite from the programme's challenge. The work went steadily on though, in my case, sometimes doggedly. I found a great difficulty in keeping going all day and every day.

Late 1938 and early 1939 were spent in fitting the Napier Schneider Trophy engine into the considerably re-built *Empire Day* to make her ready for an attempt upon the unlimited class water speed record in the coming summer.

Sir Malcolm Campbell was also preparing to improve his existing record and was busily building a new *Blue Bird*. Count Theo Rossi, backed by the Italian government, joined the line-up and seemed determined to put Italy into first place. It was thrilling, all the more so when it became apparent that the three of us were going to be ready about the same time. The London *Daily Express* referred to the forthcoming attempt as a "needle match" and "the greatest battle for marine prestige since the war."

Although it all sounded exciting, for me it was hard to believe that I was right in the middle of it. I felt more like an enthusiastic spectator watching the other two.

The manna, so kindly and generously showered at our feet by Norman Birkitt, I spent with native Yorkshire thriftiness. Every penny was made to do useful work at Slough. Any expenditure was weighed against the possible beneficial results it eventually could bring to our struggle to found a navy of superships: that was the dream we clung to.

I now designed in detail the completely new engine-integrated, power transmission system, which Shaw and I had worked out in

127

principle in 1934. This was the system that used two co-axial, oppositely rotating, high speed propellers. It was designed to take, with safety, the 940h.p. delivered by the Schneider Trophy engine. The propellers were to run at 10,000 rpm and were but eight inches in diameter. The increasing-gears, used at the top end of the drive, were taken from a return-drive gearbox, originally built by Napier's for *Estelle*, the high-speed boat built by Betty Carstairs to attempt a record-breaking crossing of the North Atlantic. The special kinds of high-speed ball and roller bearings used throughout the drive were especially designed and made for us, free of charge, by Ransome and Marles. The complete layout was a watchmaker's delight.

There were new engine cowlings and fairings to be made, a new water cooling system for the engine, larger fuel and water tanks and additional instrumentation to be worked out. Again, there were time-consuming consultations and enough drawing-board and slide rule work to keep Peter and me busy, without a break, for six months.

Furthermore, by May 1939 we had designed, built and tested, on the Thames at Isleworth, a much-simplified version of our craft, in the form of a fast two-seater, hard top, coupé boat for popular use and for river police duties. It was my fervent hope that a number of these fast little boats would sell well enough to support the cost of our continued and expensive experimental programme. However, I soon realized that if I wished to sell them in reasonable quantity I had to find a way of reducing my estimated selling price by drastically cutting production cost.

It was now glaringly evident, even to me, that I was about to make a small business venture of our work. With this realization in my mind, I tried to find a way of rocking ourselves off our stagnant, top-dead-centred, financial balance.

I disliked the thought of spending even a portion of my time making money. It was bound to be a sordid and depressing undertaking, but I could see no other way of furthering our experimental work. The work had to be paid for; so, money must be earned. I prayed that the effort would be a temporary one, I hoped in my heart that I should not be permanently corrupted by such a dreadful practice. (Time did in fact prove that in this respect I was incorruptible.)

I decided to adopt the name of a precious stone for each of the different models I intended to produce at Slough. Temporarily, as it turned out, the *Crusader* Class became the *Topaz* Class and the *Merry England* (the 100-ft express cruiser) became the *Sapphire*. There were other models and types. These included a sportsman's saloon, an open two-seater sports craft, a drop-head coupé, an open runabout, a tradesman's delivery van, a sports-racing craft, and a four-seater family saloon. The lines layouts for each of these boats had been prepared at Westminster as design exercises. At that time, I had made up a blueprint-catalogue of them which, though in poor state of preservation, is still extant.

In June, with an ulterior motive in mind, I joined Morris Motors at Oxford. I left Kes, Bob and Peter still working at Spurr Boats. In a short time, I had arranged a private interview with Viscount Nuffield. My plan was to try to get his help in supplying Spurr Boats with as much standard Morris car equipment and as many vital components as I could use in the manufacture of our small coupé boat. Because of his huge output and low production costs, I felt I might persuade him to supply us with all the components we should need for our production, at bargain prices to us. I intended to redesign our coupé model to accommodate the Morris parts should I be successful in obtaining Viscount Nuffield's approval.

In the event, the scheme I so confidently hatched was a dismal failure and wasted six weeks of valuable time. Further, much to my chagrin, few people showed any real interest in our coupé boat. In England, at that time, boats were not sold in any great quantity. They were a luxury. The boat business was a carriage and customs trade. By applying the experience I had gained in the automobile industry, I had hoped to alter these facts.

The interview itself was one I should always remember. I met Lord Nuffield (as he was generally known) in his private office at Oxford. The office appeared to be in what had been a bedroom of an old, stone-built house. It was surrounded by a stone wall and was within striking distance of the main Morris works.

I had expected to be led into a secretary's office, but Lord Nuffield himself welcomed me. He led me to a chair near his desk then sat down in his own.

There was one ordinary-sized window in the office. He told me that it was double-glazed and bullet proof. It had been installed as a safeguard against another possible attempt on his life. Not long before, somebody had taken a pot shot at him. I asked him how he had felt about the incident: he said it made him swear.

I tried hard to talk to him about my boats and his cars, how closely related they were from a manufacturing standpoint; but it wasn't easy. He seemed more inclined to talk about other things. Grasping the situation, I wasted no time in niceties (although I was polite, and kept calling him *Sir*). I blurted out my plan as quickly as I could in a matter of four or five minutes. Then I settled down to enjoy myself, for I could see that he was lonely and just wanted to talk. I was not disappointed.

Lord Nuffield turned out to be a man after my own heart. He was flesh and blood and he was an engineer. He soon confided in me that he was, by nature, a mechanic and that like Henry Ford, he thought in terms of practical mechanisms, of the common tools found on a mechanic's bench, not of fancy assembly lines.

When he learned that I was an ex-athlete of track and road, he recollected his own exploits as a racing cyclist. In his youth, he said, he had been champion of three counties and all at the same time. The medals were kept in a glass-lidded, wooden-made, display case, and there were quite a lot of them: gold, silver and bronze. Each medal had its story. One he had won when riding with a damaged ankle, another when a rear tyre burst just before he reached the FINISH line.

Suddenly, without ceremony, he pulled up his trouser leg and showed me his calf – I suppose he was well over sixty at that time – and I could still recognize the muscle might in that lower limb. Not to be outdone, I showed him my own and pointed out, while our feet were resting on his desk, the difference between a cyclist's and walker's leg muscles.

I said, as a kind of philosophical afterthought, that the great coach Sam Mussobini used to say "volume of muscle doesn't prove punishing power." With this statement, after some thought, we decided to agree.

In the end, I was with him almost all afternoon and I wouldn't have missed a single minute of it. We talked the same language, with similar emphasis. There was nothing double-distilled about Lord Nuffield. He said what he thought simply, plainly and nicely. I liked him.

By the time I left him I had gained a fairly confident feeling that, at the back of his mind, he was beginning to look upon my quickly-put plan with favour. I left his office for my digs in Oxford with jauntiness in my step. I quickly wrote Bob the good news. But, oh, was I in for a let-down!

My light-hearted assumption proved as wrong as it could be. Within a couple of days I was hauled before the managing director and given a hell of a dressing down for having the colossal nerve to contact Lord Nuffield directly.

It was plain to me that I had done what good I could do at Oxford for our cause; so I gave notice, packed up my instruments and clothing, and left the company and the city. I think I left a few friends there. My two immediate chiefs, extremely nice fellows, had been good to me. We parted on excellent terms. They told me I could re-join the company any time that I felt like it! I followed their careers for many years afterward, but I never saw them again. The name of one was Oaks, but the other's escapes me.

One of my associates in the design office at Morris Motors was a young man named Palmer. We were, I would guess, about the same age. Palmer was working on the design of an independent front wheel suspension system for the MG car while I, sitting next to him, worked on the layout of a new sheet metal front end for the Morris Minor. We became friendly, I visited his lovely old home near Oxford. He was quite rightly very proud of it. He had served his time at Scammells and showed me a small car in his garage, which he himself had designed and built. It was fitted with a small Scammell engine and it had a folding hood, which disappeared from sight when not in use. For those days it was quite new.

I relate this experience because I feel absolutely sure that this young fellow was the same Palmer who, years later, joined my *Alma*

131

Mater, Jowett Cars, and designed the Jowett *Javelin*, a flat-four engine chassis of choice automobile design.

From midsummer 1937 to the outbreak of the Second War, I had talks with many influential persons who, I thought, might be able to help me in furthering the *Crusader* project. These included: Handy Handasyde, of First War Martinsyd aircraft fame, a friend from my British Aircraft days. Handy used to say that "only birds and bloody fools fly"; Sir Malcolm Campbell, also a friend I could talk to easily; Lord Wakefield of the other Hythe, in Kent, sponsor of Sir Henry Segrave's *Miss England* boats; and Earl Howe, a keen motor-racing driver who was always kind enough to listen to my ideas, sometimes I thought, with amazement. He would have liked, he once told me, to pilot *Empire Day* on her record attempt at Windermere. I paid him the complement of stealing his racing colours for *Empire Day* – blue and silver. Many years later, I discovered that the Baxter clan's coat of arms was registered in blue and silver and that my mother, through her mother, was a Baxter. So, perhaps, I had not strayed too far from the path of heraldic decorum.

Then there was Sir Charles Craven, head of Vickers Armstrong's, whom I first met before my Windermere days. He was kind enough to get made for me at Vickers, and *gratis*, my dagger blade rudder, in 100-ton chrome alloy steel (when finished, it was a beautiful thing to behold). (Sir) Tom Sopwith, of Hawker's and of Endeavour I and II fame (challengers for the America's Cup) whom I met on two occasions at Kingston-on-Thames, kindly helped me with an important government approach. Sir John Thornycroft behaved nicely toward me. After we had had quite a heated argument over the problems of the square-cube law, he went out of his way to arrange useful government introductions for me – although I got a feeling that my ideas were a little too much for him at a first sitting.

Others with advice and encouragement were Lord Sempill, from whom I always went away feeling quiet, calm and stable; and a friend for whom I had a great regard, Mr A T Wall, managing director of Samuel White's of Cowes, who had supported me inside and outside White's on more than a score of occasions. Wall was the first man outside our own close circle to grasp the complete theory of our new kind of craft. I liked him immensely.

These men, and a few others, open-minded and courteous, generous of their time, were never against the practice of listening to a young man with a new idea.

However, nothing grew or matured from my efforts. I became more and more disappointed, especially so when I pondered the truth that the negative results were owing to my lack of ability to act the part of a persuader. How the cause needed Shaw at this time!

The talks and attachments cited had a lasting effect on me. As I, too, approached the age of seniority in my profession, I developed a warm and genuine regard for youth in general and a deep admiration for the youth in particular who finds himself advancing alone into the teeth of the gale while carrying the flag of his cherished convictions. One day, this kind of courage and dedication will be rewarded with quicker opportunity.

Older men are conservative and must be led by the nose; they play for time. Youth makes a breakthrough to higher ground with religious honesty and true conviction and does it quickly, confidently, without fearful hesitation and timid misgivings. I am not alone in my belief. Here is what (Sir) Winston Churchill wrote in *A Roving Commission*:

> Twenty to twenty-five! These are the Years! Don't be content with things as they are. 'The earth is yours and the fullness thereof.' Enter upon your inheritance, accept your responsibilities. Raise the glorious flag again, advance then upon the new enemies, who constantly gather upon the front of the human army, and have only to be assaulted to be overthrown. Don't take NO for an answer. Never submit to failure. Do not be fobbed off with mere personal success or acceptance. You will make all kinds of mistakes; but as long as you are generous and true, and also fierce, you cannot hurt the world or even seriously distress her. She may be wooed and won by youth. She has lived and survived only by repeated subjugations.

By July 1939, the international situation was looking grim and foreboding, war talk was growing furiously. I half-wondered if a grateful and repentant government, or a chastened and mollified ship industry, would ruefully embrace us and our work with heartfelt relief and apologies. No such luck. As the inevitable swiftly approached, our plans for *Empire Day II* and Lake Windermere wilted and weakened. More and more we dallied in our work at Slough as war to us seemed certain.

The bombshell fell on 3 September: we were at war. This dreadful event brought to a standstill everything we were attempting to do. Our complete project died, just when it should have been weaned. At this time, and at no time throughout the war, was the slightest official interest shown in the work that Shaw and I had so undauntedly started in those happy, sunny days of peacetime, exactly six years earlier.

Had we been financially able to keep our little factory open for the first few months of the war, small government contracts of a naval kind would, perhaps, have drifted our way. These, later, could have developed into larger assignments, leading in turn to our final dream of a supership for Britain. But it was not to be. The excitement of the war itself was too strong for us to sit passively by.

John Keats truly mirrored my thoughts of those first months of the war: "There is no fiercer hell than failure in a great cause."

Our position finally made hopeless and our spirits finally broken, we pulled down the blinds, picked up our little cat, *Peequick*, closed and locked the door of our small factory for the last time, and went our separate ways.

The dream was ended.

Chapter 10: The War Years and After

Bob Fields joined Hawker Aircraft at their factory near Slough. Peter Lynn obtained a commission in the Royal Electrical Mechanical Engineers. The last time I heard from him, he was on the Italian front and had been raised to the rank of captain. Kes Kester re-joined George Dexter at Chrysler-Dodge, although George himself later obtained a technical commission in the Royal Air Force and was given an important desk job at Whitehall. Joe Lashmar remained with Saunders Roe in the Isle-of-Wight. I used to see him once in a while, when he visited a local spot at Walton-on-Thames where I lived during most of the war. I do not know how Reggie Baines and Wally Newman fared. Norman Birkitt was kept busier than ever at his foundry; but we managed to meet occasionally when he visited London.

With regard to my own fortunes, after lengthy treatment for a duodenal ulcer, and after being turned down by the India Office for a commission in the Indian Army Ordnance Corps, in March 1940 (and again in the following May by the War Office for an appointment in the Royal Army Ordnance Corps), I joined Vickers Armstrong's, at Weybridge, on aircraft design.

I tried hard to forget boats, although the urge to continue my research did on occasion re-surface. Lord Strabolgi, on the other hand, did what he could to keep our project alive and our meagre options open. One of the wartime recommendations that he wrote to help me ran: "I have known Mr. Edward Spurr for a number of years and I have been much impressed by the importance of his research work and the investigations he is making into several aspects of naval architecture. I consider it to be in the national interest that he should be given a reasonable amount of leave to continue his research and studies."

I owed Lord Strabolgi a great debt. He went out of his busy way to make himself one of us. His help was always prompt, to the point and invaluable. As an ex-naval officer, he knew what we were talking about and he never stood on ceremony. When he died in 1953, I was deeply moved. He was a fine man, a good friend; and with his death I suffered the loss of my best adviser. I had liked him from the first moment I met him.

My wartime work at Vickers Armstrong's kept me well occupied. What spare time I could muster was used up in university studies as an external student in pure science at London. My ultimate chief at Vickers, (Sir) Barnes Wallis allowed me to take time away from my work at one period to attend special classes in military studies at Kings College in the Strand. This action of his was something special. I have always retained kind thoughts of this generous and good man.

At the time, I was working for my degree, Barnes Wallis discovered that I was taking extra lessons with University Correspondence College, Cambridge. He asked me if they were still using Briggs and Bryan's *Tutorial Algebra.* I assured him they were. As a young man studying for his own degree at London, he too had been a student of this college. As I write, I have a short note resting on my desk. He penned it to me during this study period of mine. It reads, "Dear Spurr, Just a line of good wishes for your ultimate success, B N W."

While at Vickers, I recollect one day idly flexing a thin, steel corset stay between my fingers. Without thought, I bent it over and held both ends together between finger and thumb. It struck me that its shape formed a pretty good streamline form. Out of mild interest, I drew around the shape with a finely pointed lead pencil. I then proportionally elongated the trace on a separate piece of paper to a fineness ratio of five-to-one.

The result was astounding. My trained eye told me that the shape was close to perfection. On the same piece of paper, on the same ordinates and centre line, to the same scale, I drew the near-ideal streamline form for subsonic airflow, which had been developed experimentally by the National Advisory Committee for Aeronautics, in America.[4] I was surprised and fascinated to observe that the variation was indeed minute. I spent time trying mathematically to relate this new curve to the streamline flow around

---

[4]   Edward P. Warner, *Airplane Design: Performance,* pp 348-9, McGraw-Hill, 1936, 2nd Ed.

it, hoping to demonstrate purely by mathematics the ideal low resistance form for subsonic flow. For example, I tried to find a link between the bending stresses and strains of a tip-held lamina strip and the pressures brought about by the air velocities over its surface - as indicated by the Bernoulli theorem. It was beyond me. My parameters failed me; my wits proved inelastic.

I thought my observation might interest B N W, who had a brilliant mathematician at his side, Mrs. Hore. When I got the chance I showed him my sketch. He looked, and listened to all I had to say, but passed no helpful comment. Perhaps he had his mind on more pressing matters.

I have the sketch in front of me. I found it as a bookmark in my Warner's *Airplane Design*. As I look at it, I am still as intrigued as I was almost forty years ago. Perhaps, now that I have described my observation and admitted my failure to rationalize it mathematically, somewhere, someday, some bright young man will make sense of what I could not. I am absolutely sure that the parallel is too close merely to be coincidental; it is too beautiful to be untrue.

Barnes Wallis was responsible for what became known world-wide as the Dambusters project. This venture was the fantastic air raid into Germany, which used the unique Wallis, pot-bellied, athwartship-spinning, bouncing bomb, which successfully breached the Moehne and Eder Dams in the Ruhr Valley, on 16/17 May 1943. In less than two days I made an original layout for him of a proposed rotating mechanism for the bomb. The final design, I believe, closely adhered to this hasty layout. For leading the flight, Wing Commander Guy Gibson was awarded the Victoria Cross.

Again, it was Barnes Wallis who gave me the chance, under Jack Thorne, to design the first flying test-bed-installation for a jet engine, the (Sir) Frank Whittle W.2b unit. We installed this unique power unit in place of the rear gunner's compartment at the tail end of a Vickers *Wellington* bomber. The main piston engines remained undisturbed in the wings; the bomb-bays were used for carrying the kerosene fuel tanks required for the jet engine. The flight tests took place at Hucknall, near Nottingham, under the auspices of Rolls-Royce.

Our experimental manager of those days, (Sir) George Edwards, built the Whittle jet engine installation to my design. He used to call it the *Squirter*. I can still see him, in my mind's eye, looking down at my drawing board and talking about the "cosine effect". My board was situated in a *cul-de-sac* off the open corridor at the Burhill Golf Club House, immediately opposite the front door. It was bitterly cold in the winter and George Edwards wondered why I bore it out. I liked it because, although it was open at my back to the door, it was quiet and secluded. The Burhill Golf Club House, where we back-room boys worked throughout the war, had been the home of the Duke of Wellington, victor of the Battle of Waterloo.

George Edwards had broken away from our design staff "chain gang" and had gone on to bigger and more responsible duties as a result of his brilliantly successful de-gaussing ring system, used on our aircraft for detonating German magnetic sea-mines. These mines were causing havoc in our coastal shipping lanes during the first six weeks of the war. It was a job well done, his promotion to experimental manager was earned and deserved. In my mind's eye, I picture Sir George Edwards at his persuasive best when acting as Britain's leading negotiator for the Concorde supersonic airliner.

These were engrossing days for all of us at Vickers, full of interest and high, blood and battle related, endeavour.

I recall an incident that reminds me of my family's introduction to the modern art of indiscriminate bombing – nonchalantly referred to in the military classroom as "an extension of foreign policy". In the middle of the night we were awakened by the thumping and exploding of bombs all around us. Realizing, after a couple of seconds, what was happening, I jumped out of bed, noticing that my kneecaps were dancing up and down like Mexican beans. I was shocked at myself for not being able to control them. I wasn't terrified; but I was frightened. Then, I thought I heard the clinking of milk bottles as our delivery boy noisily put them on our back door step. What an odd time to be delivering milk, I thought. The clinking sound turned out to be the jostling together of hundreds of falling fire bombs. Luckily, none fell on our roof.

Three years after this first baptism, we were bombed out of our home. It happened one afternoon in June; and it was a flying bomb.

I saw it in the distance, heading for Shaldon Way, and knew instinctively it was "ours". I had counted more than ten of them coming up the centre of our road in the previous sixty minutes. We scrambled into our indoor shelter. The bang came as I, the last one in, got my heels under the steel plating. Seconds later, I went out into the road and saw that the whole area was nothing but a battlefield. I couldn't believe it. But there it was. Some of our neighbours were dead.

When at work, it was a habit of mine not to go to the company shelter during a bombing raid but, instead, to make my way on to the golf course. Once there, lying on my back in the grass, with my hands clasped at the back of my head for comfort and relaxation, I would watch the action in the sky. On one occasion, a damp, dark, misty, miserable morning, I continued to work at my drawing board during the alert. After a time, and with no warning, I sensed a visitor at my back. It was R K Pierson, our chief designer.

"R K", as a younger man, had designed the first aircraft to fly the Atlantic Ocean, the Vickers *Vimy*. This aircraft, flown from Newfoundland to Ireland by Capt. (Sir) John Alcock (pilot), and Lieut. (Sir) Arthur Whitten Brown (navigator), on 14-15 June 1919, had been designed originally as a bomber; but special modifications to the machine had made it suitable for the magnificent cross-Atlantic flight it had accomplished.

R K leant over my shoulder and said, "Why aren't you in the shelter, Spurr?" This was, of course, a company regulation; but suddenly, seeing the irony of the situation, I found the courage to say, "What about yourself, Sir?" He hesitated, then smiled broadly, and walked away. I liked him; and he was good enough to sponsor me for membership in the Royal Aeronautical Society. I always envied R K his panchromatic-grey Rolls-Bentley.

On and off I toyed with the idea of one day building a jet-powered boat for the water speed record. After all, was I not one of the first of the few to know about the existence of such an original and exciting power plant? I had enough knowledge of it to be able to assess its advantages for such an application. The idea was attractive and spectacular. I could see that Shaw's and my principle of employing substantial air support could not be used in this instance.

139

At the contemplated speeds of 400 mph or more, using a lightweight craft, the problem would be to keep the boat in reasonable and controllable contact with the water surface. The problems fascinated me; it was because of them that I decided to investigate the feasibility of such a craft.

At the end of the war, with some jet knowledge having come into the open, Sir Malcolm Campbell told me that he was planning an attempt on the unlimited class record with his existing 3-pointer *Blue Bird* boat, fitted with a jet engine instead of his Rolls-Royce piston unit. I then told him that I too had had similar ideas for the past three years.

In a letter to me about this time (Sept.1945) Sir Malcolm wrote, "...any speed which may be achieved in the near future on land or water by cars or craft propelled by orthodox methods will be raised by huge margins when jet propulsion is adopted: propeller drive has always appeared to me to be so antiquated; and very little improvement in propeller design has been made over a long period of years."

"In the case of *B. Bird,* we get 20% slip which is very good as things go: ships like the *Queen Mary* get a greater percentage of loss than this. To me it seems all wrong that such a high percentage of loss should occur..."

By February, 1948, after much disappointment with his early tests of jet propulsion, he changed his ideas radically, for then he wrote me, "All my tank tests have been carried out in the Admiralty experimental tank at Haslar and the relative highest speed which has been achieved with a very small model was equivalent to 160 m.p.h. However, we all know of the Gibson scale, the smaller the model used the less you can rely upon the results achieved. In our instance, we cannot reproduce the various factors which arise, such as the change of temperature, the velocity of the gas emitted aft of the jet, nor the effect the rush of air has on the prow of the boat, as it is being sucked into the supercharger. There is no question that, notwithstanding the advantages of having no propeller and no waterscoop, the disadvantages more than outweigh those on the credit side."

However, as it turned out, Sir Malcolm made no more attempts on the water speed record after his disappointing trials of 1947.

Sir Malcolm's son Donald, whom I met only once when he was a very young boy, later demonstrated the definite advantages of the jet-powered boat for sprint purposes. In his specially constructed, outrigger-sponsoned *Blue Bird* he attained extremely high speeds – in the neighbourhood of 300 mph. Unfortunately, he finally pressed this craft, so I was told, beyond its maximum designed speed. So it was that his magnificent series of successes over the years ended in tragedy.

Donald Campbell's craft had literally taken off from the water surface and then capsized. This was the dreaded possibility I had tried to prevent with my own investigation during the war years. Be that as it may, Sir Malcolm himself would have been very proud of his son Donald. They were, indeed, very truly, the Flying Campbells.

In late 1944, I got the opportunity to return to Yorkshire. It was like being in heaven to live in peace and quiet again after the years of aerial assault and pandemonium that we had endured in the London area. It was nice to meet old friends and relatives again. But two years there, in the rain and snow, were enough to revive my wartime yearning for sunshine. Throughout the war I had displayed, near to my desk, to perk up my spirits, an empty suitcase with a beautifully coloured label on it, for all to see. It said *RIO DE JANEIRO*.

Even as early as 13 December 1945, a day on which I met Lord Strabolgi in the House of Lords, I was already seriously eyeing a map of the world for sunny spots where I might make a passable living. That day, we had tea in the lounge and, among other things, I told him that I was operating my own small, patents holding company and manufacturing business, but that I was seriously considering making a fresh start abroad. I said that I was not happy battling against the then manufacturing restrictions, shortages of essential materials and the "blasted" weather. He told me that the restrictions and frustrations were here to stay for a while, that the shortage of materials would continue and that it was a pound to a pinch of snuff that the "blasted" weather in Bradford wouldn't change its pattern. "If you really must make a complete change", he said, "why not consider sunny South Africa?"

Lord Strabolgi told me he knew the country and that the prospects for me would be good. Johannesburg was a go-ahead city which would keep me on my toes and offer me professional satisfaction of high degree. Until Lord Strabolgi had suggested South Africa, I had never even fingered it on my map, never mind considered it as a serious place for re-settlement. I bore it in mind and later looked into it.

At the beginning of 1947, full of trepidation, I was fast approaching my finals for a B.Sc. Special in mathematics at London. In early 1945, Lord Strabolgi had introduced me to Professor Brodetsky, head of the applied mathematics department at the University of Leeds. Professor Brodetsky had taken me under hand. At his own home, in his meagre spare time, at no cost to me, he struggled and wrestled to augment my native ability in mathematics, in a determined effort to instil a little of Einstein's genius into my addled but now eager brain. I have a lot to thank him for. Whatever higher mathematics I have been able to command is largely owing to his help and guidance.

I was delighted when, later, Professor Brodetsky was given the Chair in mathematics at the University of Jerusalem, a post he valued highly. Before going to Jerusalem, he wrote me, "I hope that before long you will be able to try and establish new world records. It is nice for me to think of a man who makes world records while struggling with conics and equations!"

I have been extraordinarily lucky in my choice of friends, teachers and co-workers. Without these happy choices, my modest talent for design could not have flourished with any strength or broadened into the passion that it did. Design has been my life, and without it I would have been a miserable soul.

On a chilly day in May 1947, I finally pulled up roots in England and began to chase the sun in earnest. I sailed for South Africa, and a new life. My wife Edwina, and my young son John – by that time he was nine years old – sailed a few weeks later, joining me at Vanderbijl Park, near Vereeniging, in the Transvaal.

From the moment I walked off the gang plank at Cape Town, where I was welcomed with a cup of tea by a kind, elderly hostess, I gloried in my new surroundings. Once off the ship, walking and sightseeing along Adderley Street, I saw oranges, bananas, and coconuts in sun-drenched windows and Swiss watches on the jewellers' counters. I hadn't seen such luxuries for seven years; and, unbelievably to me, there was no rationing.

It was just like Fairyland. The climate, the jobs, the homes, the cleanliness, the immense amount of space, the wonderful people of all nations, colours and creeds, made me wonder how I had managed to live and be happy anywhere else. The people were hard working, generous and kind. Making friends was easy and always rewarding. Altogether, my small family and I spent more than nine years in South Africa. They were happy and fruitful years. I shall always think of that wonderful country with great affection and high regard.

After a modest beginning as a mechanical designer at the Vanderbijl Engineering Corporation at Vanderbijl Park, I founded, in late 1947, a small design company of my own. I named it Industrial Designs (Pty) Ltd. Later, in 1950, this small company became a subsidiary of the largest group of companies in South Africa at that time, the Industrial and Commercial Holdings Group, Ltd., and its name was changed to Edispur, Ltd.

During the short time I was employed at VECOR, I managed to talk some of the apprentices in the pattern shop into making a wind tunnel model of my proposed, jet-powered, speedboat. They sculpted it beautifully; it accurately reflected the findings of my war years' investigations, the results of which I had already referred to Sir Malcolm Campbell. The model was placed on exhibition at the famous Rand Show in 1948, although I did not, for the Exhibition, permit the underwater sections to be seen, or the low drag, negative lift, water surface retainer system. This model is extant, but in poor condition after many years' use as a magazine weight and doorstop.

In England, immediately after the war, I had seized another opportunity for improving my all-round ability as a designer, one that served me well during my years in South Africa. Through the auspices of the Council for Industrial Design, I received at

Hoddesdon Hall, in Hertfordshire, a short intensive course in industrial design, with direct application to the design of new consumer products. Years later, when they made exploratory visits to South Africa in 1952-54, I was to coach two of my tutors from Hoddesdon Hall in some of my own special techniques in design. I remember the demonstration I gave them in the use and beauty of the quadratic curves. These curves, to my mind, are just as important to the designer as the classical Parthenon rectangle.

I became the first practising designer to apply and professionally promote the art and science of industrial design in South Africa. It was a labour of love and a delight; my reward was the intense satisfaction I got and the growth it showed by the time I left Africa nine years later.

While at Vanderbijl Park, I had taught mechanical design to indentured apprentices. This was a voluntary, unpaid evening job, which I genuinely enjoyed. The apprentices were a talented group and they were serious students. As a result, I was asked to undertake similar duties at the Vereeniging Technical College; but I felt I was right in turning down such a misguided request. Heaven knows, I am no teacher, not really. I can teach only in passing. I have no talent for making a routine of it.

In the middle of 1948, I talked to Dr. Vanderbijl about the research work I had done on high-speed ships. He appeared to be genuinely interested in all that I told him. He asked me to write him a short report outlining the state of my art up to the point I had then reached. He asked me to relate the report to the possible development of an advanced form of high speed navy, a navy suitable for the defence of South Africa on both its coasts. I remember that he was keen to know if the new ships could be used as miniature aircraft carriers.

I liked Dr. Vanderbijl. He had taken me very seriously; listened attentively; made many notes and had asked me the kind of questions I appreciated. He struck me as being logical and thorough. I knew that my time had not been wasted.

I worked hard at the report, as often as I could manage to do so, but long before it approached completion, Dr. Vanderbijl was taken seriously ill, lingered for a time, then died. It was, therefore,

144

all to no avail. With his death, South Africa lost a good man, America a good friend, and I an ideal sponsor.

I designed everything that came my way: exhibition stands, cameras, light and heavy mining equipment, aerial magnetometers, portable gramophones, domestic washing machines, racing boats, small cars, toasters, heaters, fire proof safes, combination locks, hodograph machines, aluminium racehorse shoes, collapsible radar masts, stainless steel products of all kinds, high speed gearing, grain conveyors (structures and mechanisms), display mechanisms and a hundred other things.

I conducted the management of a new products experimental and development laboratory and a prototype assembly and pilot shop. During the same period, I was chief consulting engineer to a group of companies producing, among other things: artificial jewellery, gramophone records, crayons and devotional candles, blood plasma, plastic floors tiles and garden hoses, car batteries, air conditioners, and general engineering hardware.

I cannot now fully recollect all the designs, products and processes for which I was responsible; but I remember the years themselves for the good life they gave me, both on and off the drawing board, in and out of the laboratory and factory.

The drawing board was always my first choice of vocation. Consulting and advising commitments, managerial duties, and committee work, were distracting chores and necessary job routines, rather than sought-for delights.

The last link in my partnership with Aircraftman Shaw was forged and completed while I was living in South Africa. In 1949, I was honoured by being elected to the council of the Royal Aeronautical Society (Southern Africa Division) and, soon afterward, I was asked if I would care to offer a paper for presentation before the society in early 1950. Although delighted to acquiesce, I was alarmed at the thought of having to deliver it. As may be expected, I forthwith wrote the long-delayed paper I had promised Shaw in 1934. I entitled it *Aircraft Principles and Practice as Aids to Future Speed Boat Design*, and I presented it at Kelvin House, Johannesburg, on the evening of 15 February 1950.

145

The paper took the form of a summary of the investigations we made sixteen years earlier, concentrating on the hydrodynamics rather than the aerodynamics of our work. It showed our method of approach solving the basic hydrodynamic problems of the planing boat; and demonstrated how the already established and clearly defined aerodynamic data of the aeroplane could be selected and transformed for the understanding of the hydrodynamics of the speed boat, just as Shaw had intuitively foreseen.

I made no attempt, in the limited time available, to describe our boat as such, although the craft was depicted in diagrammatic form in order to demonstrate the general balance of forces required for dynamic equilibrium. As a result of this treatment of the paper, I believe I was successful in presenting and portraying it in the form that Shaw would have wished.

However, looking back over my shoulder, I now wish that I had touched upon the very special aerodynamics of our new kind of hull. Perhaps at the time I wrote the paper, I was not keen to divulge the full picture of our research, and so stuck only to what Shaw had asked of me.

Strangely, as with the rest of our work, the paper languished in oblivion from the day it was delivered. I am sure that had it been circulated freely, then a number of high speed fatalities that took place on the water in the years just ahead could have been avoided. I had emphasized, for example, that all the running lines under the hull of an extremely fast planing boat should be kept straight and parallel to each other in order to avoid deadly "suction loads". This observation, to the expert, also suggests that even a simple bow curve should be made up of a series of straight, and not too short, feather steps, instead of the usual simple continuous curve. This downward, parallel, straight-line, formation of its lines for a planing surface, or a feather step, is vitally important to preserve a positive downwash at every step at all running trims. At high speeds a convex curve can be the key that opens the door to sudden tragedy by generating a negative downwash angle (in every-day language, a strong and powerful "suction load").

I was careful to avoid using Shaw's name, in the hope that no sensational comments would be encouraged either at the meeting or,

146

more particularly, the next day in the press. Experience had taught me to be discreet in this matter, especially so with regard to the use of the descriptive appellation *Lawrence of Arabia*. This title, though well-deserved and highly appropriate, when used before even a normally well-adjusted and sophisticated group of listeners, could induce a demand for answers to the most fantastic questions concerning his life. Nervous and incompetent as I am before an audience, I wanted no such embarrassment. To me, Shaw was a fellow engineer; it was in this respect, and no other, that I knew him.

To my relief, the paper was appreciatively, yet quietly, received; and I was thankful. I was grateful to Professor Walker, head of the mechanical department of the University of the Witwatersrand, for taking the Chair. He complimented me publicly and privately for my paper, saying that he rated it one of "uncommonly high calibre and fascinating originality". Such commendation was music to my ears and praise enough; I wish Shaw could have heard it.

Professor Walker told me that he thought I stood a good chance of earning the gold medal award of the Southern Africa division for the paper. But I never did. I admit that I was a little disappointed; but perhaps it was just as well. The honour would have gone to my head; I should have had the frightening task of accepting it, on a raised dais, in front of an audience.

I looked upon the writing and the delivery of the paper as representing, under the rose, my *à compte II to L. of A.*

Chapter 11: *Amende Honorable* and Farewell to a Courageous Lady

Since the death of Shaw in May, 1935, I have practised my profession in forty different locations and I have resided in four different countries. During those years, I have led the full and busy life of a working designer. I never thought for a moment that one day I should feel compelled to give an account of my work with him. I believed, even many years ago, that what we had done together, and what I had steadfastly continued to do until the summer of 1939, was deeply in-earthed and long forgotten.

H F King's[5] interest in delving into our research, and then ventilating his discoveries, has persuaded me to record more of the details and some of the background of those industrious though, toward the end, disappointing years. What I have written will, perhaps, be useful in three ways: I believe that I have clearly demonstrated Shaw's keen insight and natural talent as an engineer and innovator; I have offered additional detail concerning Shaw and his activities during the last eighteen months of his career in the RAF; and I have presented a first-hand and more precise history of our joint work (and the background that went with it) than the excellent, though necessarily barer, outline given by Mr King, for those who find interest in chronological detail.

Owing to my roving life I have rarely been able to hold on to memorabilia of any kind. When I left Bradford to settle in South Africa, my home was sold completely furnished. In the haste and excitement at the thought of going to live and work in lovely, warm sunshine, in a new, delightful and growing country – my first such experience – I left behind, on my shelves and high cupboards: models, test equipment, letters, notes and sketches, test reports, calculation sheets and photographs connected with Shaw's and my days at Hythe in Southampton.

---

[5] *Another Lawrence, "Aircraftman Shaw" and Air-Cushion Craft*, by H.F. King, MBE. *Flight International* Supplement, 24 February 1966.

I had been given less than three weeks to settle my affairs in England. In that short time I had to satisfy and complete South Africa's immigration requirements, sell my home and contents, pack my baggage, get to the quayside at Southampton and aboard the *Winchester Castle*. With a rush, but no fineness, I did it. Of the memorabilia relating to my association with Shaw, I took only what I thought I might someday need. Everything else was left. At the time this decision didn't seem to be an important one.

For many years my Bradford home had been the vicarage of St. Augustine's Church, in Otley Road, before I bought it. It was a home that was perfectly designed for losing memorabilia. It was old, three storeys high, with a basement; stone-built; massive in its smooth-dressed solidarity, full of spacious nooks and crannies. Perhaps it still stands and still conceals.

Of the relics and mementos I managed to take with me to South Africa, most were placed for safe keeping with a relative in Durban when nine years later I left Africa to experiment with life in America. These items were cast away almost in their entirety fourteen years later when, in turn, the relative who was looking after them decided to leave South Africa and settle in the United States. Among these discarded pieces were three of the solid-type, test models – special to me because of their full complement of appendages and built-on test equipment. Original design layouts, sheets of tabulated hull geometries, aerodynamic and hydrodynamic data and some letters of special, historical interest, all disappeared. A few items *do* remain to remind me of those busy days: test model photographs (wood and clay); bound, but uncompleted, technical notes; graphs of all kinds; about a thousand newspaper clippings in a battered album; a letter or two; copies of the patents and design registrations; photographs of the layouts of the original *Empire Day* (with a Rolls Royce R-type engine, but never built) and *Crusader*; a couple of scale drawings on cartridge paper – the single-propeller power transmission system as used at Windermere; a lay-out of the 100-ft. torpedo boat; a catalogue of proposed general production craft for the Spurr Boat Company of Slough, made up of blueprints bound together; and, finally, the two, now historically interesting, display models, sadly in need of expert renovation by some hand

149

steadier than mine. Perhaps one day, they will be accepted, restored, and placed in a safe resting place for historical interest. Their importance in this respect will, I think, grow with the years.

The last time I saw *Empire Day II* was the year the war ended. She was lying on the hard, bare, concrete floor of a brass foundry at Stoke-on-Trent, thickly covered in foundry dust. The magnificent Napier Schneider Trophy engine was still intact in her noble shell, but her bridge-like cradle, built so carefully and so lovingly by Bob Fields, was gone.

As I viewed, in her distress, this still fair craft, I could not but think of other courageous beauties of history and of their decline and passing – some regally and nobly, others sadly and tragically. *Empire Day*, beauty that she was, was slowly dying, not of old age or by weight of acclaim, but of past struggles and shameful neglect. For her, there would be no lasting memory. But for the bounded memories of the young men who had courted her in the days of her youth, she would be gone and forever forgotten. Born of a dream, she would go back to a dream and the dream would fade into nothing.

It took me longer than I would have guessed to bring myself to gaze into her always lonely cockpit. In that once sparklingly clean, but severe and confined space, I had spent the most exhilarating and, at the last, the most deliberately hurried seconds in my life. Even now, more than half a lifetime later, my heartbeat quickens with those memories.

Reflectively, and with no one looking on, I took my pocket-handkerchief and wiped away the thick dust from her streamline nose, just beneath the engine's air intake. Proudly, out blazed the red, white and blue of the Union Jack. Wiped again, just a little lower, the inscription read:

EMPIRE DAY II
To L. of A.: à compte

I turned away, smothering my emotions of those final, intimate moments with her, and tried hard to think only of her glorious days when her admirers came from far and wide to elbow their way toward her for a closer glimpse of what our friends in the press had called the "wonder craft" and the "magic boat from Lawrence's plans". Once I turned away, I never looked back.

Out on the street the wind was cold, the rain incessant. And for once in my life, I couldn't find anything to laugh about.

Chapter 12: Late Autumn and the End of the Road

At Johannesburg in November 1955, after many and perhaps over busy-years in South Africa, I suffered a heart attack.

By the time I was taken ill I had seen much of southern Africa; but, after a lengthy recovery period, I decided to follow a long-intended wish to complete a closer viewing of the fascinating sub-continent. It was an adventure to enjoy and I did so. I ended by gaining a first-hand knowledge of life in the Transvaal, Natal, the Orange Free State, the Cape Province, Swaziland, Portuguese East Africa, South West Africa and both Rhodesias. Then, afterwards, back into modest harness again, I decided to slow down the *tempo* of my life and from then on live quietly. I made up my mind, as Shaw had done, to take orders and, for evermore, never again to give them. In this I became reasonably successful.

I had too many friends and too many active interests in that wonderful country ever to be able to live there in total obscurity and undisturbed tranquillity. Our small family decided, once again, to pull up roots and seek a quiet life in America, on the California coast. It was an experiment I had always wanted to make; but at the age of almost fifty, it was a chancy decision to take. This risk, however, worried none of us, for we had always relished minor adventures which offered a change of environment in our lives. John, then eighteen, was delighted to try the move and so was I.

Unbelievably, once settled in Santa Monica, we found it easier to lead and enjoy an unnoticed existence than in any other place we had previously lived in. It might be that this was owing to the reality that life in the United States is so competitive and the struggle for personal recognition so strong, that an easy-going, half-recluse, such as I wanted to be, was enabled without any great difficulty, to lose himself in the keenly ambitious throng and thereby painlessly avoid unwanted, over-ambitious challenges.

Our introduction to life in America took place in the late summer of 1956 although our acclimatization was not immediate or effortless. On our arrival in New York the high level of noise stunned me, by night as well as by day, and by the almost demoniacal hurry and concentration with which everyone went about his business. There was no gushing friendliness and little eye-to-eye recognition. After the matey-ness of Yorkshire and the easy warmth of South Africa, this was a little disconcerting. In California I was surprised to see every other fellow wearing denims. I wondered if we had landed ourselves among a nation of boilermakers. Some even hobbled along in sharp-toed, fancy-patterned, high-heel cowboy boots and funny, wide, roll-rimmed hats. I'm sure they were tall and bowlegged to a man. I wondered would I too, in due course, have to embrace this raw *macho* image? I shrink from anything that reminds me of the cruelty of the rodeo.

We had a lot to learn. We found America to be somewhat more impersonal than England, South Africa or, later, Australia. Most Americans seemed to us to take life too seriously; the monthly pay cheque seemed to be deified out of all proportion to its true value in relation to the good life it was supposed to bestow.

Later, I came to understand and sympathize with the fears that lay behind these American traits and behavioural tendencies when I learned, from still fearful witnesses, of the suffering, hardship and ruin that had resulted from the 1929 economic crash. It will take a long time for those distressing experiences to soften and blur in the American memory. I came to realize how little I knew about hard times. During the big American depression, I, in England, had not lost a single day's work. Others I knew had got by on "short time". We had indeed been fortunate.

After two years in Santa Monica, where I once again worked on the design of gas turbines (this time with Propulsion Research Corporation – a subsidiary of Curtiss-Wright), I found myself in the midst of one of the periodical recessions in business so familiar to the American.

We jumped at the opportunity to wander again. This time we visited Australia (another long-held desire) and stayed for a year before returning to Santa Monica, by which time the business climate had improved. Many companies were beginning, once again, to hire and expand. I joined the Advance Development Division of the McCulloch Corporation, at Los Angeles, under the direct and admirable leadership of the vice president of research, Jim Dooley.

Once again, I was fortunate. Right from the start Jim and I got along well. In between times we squeezed in many a hearty laugh – always a good pick-me-up in the middle of a sticky design or research problem.

Robert McCulloch, a qualified engineer and designer of ability, was known throughout the western world as the purchaser of London Bridge. Stone by marked stone, he re-erected the bridge at Lake Havasu City in Arizona, the city he founded and built on the Colorado River. As a friendly limey, though a somewhat de-tribalized one, I cajoled a gullible friend of mine, who was close to the rebuilding operation at Havasu, to "knock off" (there is, I think, a kind of comforting difference between *knocking off* and *stealing*) a small chip of the historic bridge for my own possession. Whenever, in my rummaging, I come across this small piece of old London, I gaze upon it with nostalgic rapture.

I spent ten years, on and off, with Jim Dooley at the McCulloch Advance Development Division. We designed, built and tested the strangest of power units and the oddest of mechanisms. If I were to describe any one of these delightful experimental ventures in detail, I would take the chance of being scoffed at in disbelief. All these precision-built originals were engineered as part of the McCulloch wisdom of investigating the future possibilities of any mechanism or power plant that promised marked improvement over contemporary designs. Our job at the A.D.D was to look into the blue with unabashed boldness. And that we did.

Our specialty was the development of the two-stroke engine for all kinds of purposes – tiny chainsaw units, up to moderately-sized aircraft power plants, both petrol and Diesel. By unwritten law, however, there was one line of research that was firmly closed to us – four-stroke engines. As vomit on the rose, so was the four-stroke engine anathema to our conscience.

I think that Jim's and my favourite funny engine was a square-piston, paddle-connecting-rod unit – as I called it. This was the only engine I ever developed, or know of, that had its air intake port open to the atmosphere and fully functioning for a complete revolution of its crankshaft. It gobbled in all the air it could use with minimum loss of mechanical energy.

The years at McCulloch's were good ones. My time was spent on design; engine test work and in the laboratory, where I engineered my own designs. Jim Dooley knew my outlook and allowed me to hide what little light I could claim for myself under a simple titular bushel. Whatever supervision and direction I felt compelled to give, I gave from below; in that way I avoided real responsibility.

During the years since the death of Shaw I have, whenever time would permit and for the simple enjoyment of exercising the designer's insatiable desire for improvement, turned my thoughts to the fond task of trying to expand and extend Shaw's and my earlier ideas in such a way that they could be used for the development of a modern, high speed, space-age navy. These intermittent but nevertheless persistent diversions over fifty years became pleasant distractions from the more serious cares and duties of a busy, working designer. During these quiet moments I lived, once again, with Shaw at my elbow and, once again, the results were unique.

And now it is time for me to end my narrative for, as Jim Fisk, New York's colourful nineteenth century financial buccaneer used to say, "The woodbine twineth ... over the old tin oven"; and I might add, unlike Mother Nature, old men do not live forever to tell their tale.

Sometimes when I look over the ocean, I daydream. I see myself as a young man and there, standing nearby, I see another man. He is older than I and he wears a faded sports jacket – a little baggy at the elbows - a roll-neck sweater and grey slacks. And I see a ship: a sleek, fast one, in royal blue and silvered aluminium. The man in the sweater is bare-headed; his hair is blustering in the wind. I can see one of his hands clasping the wrist of the other behind him and he is smiling.

Would he now, on second thoughts, prefer the clean and undefiled sea to the hard and stony desert? I like to think so.

One day perhaps, and not too far distant, I shall find out for sure.

And now, with welcome relief and a debtor's burden shed, I can with some truth, claim my duty ended and the commitment of my youth honoured. So, *actum et tractatum*, which, as everybody knows, means: DONE AND PERFORMED

The Russian ekranoplan (aka "The Caspian Sea Monster") first flew in the mid-1960s. Twice as big and heavy as any existing aircraft, it exploited 'ground effect' for added lift in ways that Spurr first explored. It was like a huge flying boat with stubby wings, and flew much like Spurr's idea of "a flying boat just before take-off." In fact, the Russian Embassy approached Spurr while at Lake Windermere, presumably to 'borrow' his technology, but he ignored them. The planned military use of such ekranoplans was very much in line with Shaw's ideas of fast attack and invasion. Flying at surface level, the ekranoplan is very difficult to detect by radar and, of course, rides over minefields. How it might be affected by the swells and waves of oceans is not clear.

The banks of engines at the front direct their jets over the upper surface of the stub wings, enhancing the lift they provide. Beneath the wings the air is trapped between wing and water, increasing the air pressure and thus increasing lift. Thus the ekranoplan can lift much heavier loads than an aeroplane but can still travel at up to 400mph.

Perhaps these are among the developments in the future that Spurr foresaw in some of his enigmatic statements.

Epilogue: My Recollections of T E Shaw

I consider it an advantage to have met T E Shaw long after he had become famous as T E Lawrence. His greatest work had been completed at least fifteen years earlier; by the time I met him he was approaching his retirement as an aircraftman, still of the lowest rank: an A/c2, from the Royal Air Force. At this time, his life was a quiet one and free from tension. Best of all, I met him through his hobby, for that is what fast boats had come to mean to him. Often, to know a man through his hobby or his closest interest simplifies a relationship, and for this reason I came to know Shaw in his more relaxed moods. This was a great benefit to me during the unduly short time that lay ahead.

Although not tall, about five-foot-six at the most, I never felt conscious of his lack of height – perhaps because I am but a modest five-foot-nine myself. Fair haired and blue eyed, his complexion was fresh, like that of a seaman's. His lips were full, but straight and firm, and his jaw was strongly-contoured and resolute. He kept his hair "unstyled", cut in the RAF "short, back and sides" tradition. His face, I thought, showed strength and natural dignity; but in it I sometimes caught a look of what I thought could be called spiritual loneliness. To me, as a young man of some *naïveté,* this look was beyond my direct understanding although I felt its effect when I saw it. Fleetingly, it would put distance between us. In later years, when I thought about it, I came to think of it as the subconscious reflection of a searing and cruel habit of introspection which had been practised over a long period of time.

I recollect Shaw best when I picture him wearing his straw-brown, Harris Tweed jacket; his grey, roll-necked sweater; and his grey sports slacks. The slacks were worn somewhat short – or so, in my judgment, they seemed to me. I was accustomed to wearing my own bags well over the instep. In civvies he always looked neat in appearance and strongly masculine, but with that touch of disarray seen in the undergraduate of the Thirties. In his A/c2 uniform, he looked noticeably well-groomed. The uniform fitted flawlessly, as though tailor-made for him; and with his shining boots and burnished buttons, he represented traditional RAF spit-and-polish to perfection. His salute before a senior officer was smart, precise and unsmiling – on the outside.

When I talked to Shaw, his gaze would vary little. He would look directly but fleetingly into my eyes as I was making a point of interest to him; he would then look down and ponder awhile, as he further considered what I had said. The reply would not always be immediate – in the things we talked about – but when it came it was never vague or evasive. His voice was quiet, slightly high-pitched and finely controlled; I often thought I detected a slight accent or inflection that could have been Irish or Welsh. It was too slight to distinguish accurately; but if I was compelled to make a firm guess, I would plump for Irish (I am quite good at recognizing accents).

He often talked in the casual manner of an undergraduate and seemed purposely to avoid the use of precise textbook nomenclature. When he talked of boats and engines, a boat had a sharp and blunt end (or front and back), a lower and an upper floor, a right and left-hand side; and engines and cogs instead of gears, valve holes instead of valve ports; a clutch could be dry or juicy. It was his way, I believe, of making conversation easy; I was never deluded into thinking it technical illiteracy.

Owing to the legend behind Shaw, I always thought of him as a man of instant and physical action – I think all at the yard did – although I witnessed only quiet, almost concealed, activity by him. Nevertheless, even that kind of action was executed swiftly, with no explanation; and it always ended with the result he had planned.

In matters of intrigue and manoeuvre, he never gave up until he had got what he wanted. All approaches toward the end he had set his mind on would be considered carefully and dispassionately; even a minor battle of wits would be played out like a game of chess. It was impossible to guess what was in his mind on these occasions; but it was always pretty certain that he was three moves ahead of his opposition. As I was a young engineer with my head full of mechanics, I was never sufficiently adept at analysing the thrusts and timings of his stratagems. I noticed enough, from time to time, to be filled with awe at the neatness, deftness and success of the results he attained. Without doubt, Shaw could, whenever he wished, bamboozle the devil himself; and he often did, with no fear and much glee.

I noticed that Shaw, like Julius Caesar, Hannibal and Alexander the Great, was a master of the indirect approach. This was plain to see, even in everyday affairs. When, in any plan he had conceived, his considered move came, it was unexpected, quick, and decisive. Accordingly, had he lived a little longer, I am sure our own work would have been accepted by the Admiralty as a firm basis for further high-speed ship research. With Shaw at the helm of our request, however determined and obstinate the opposition might have been, neither mental inertia nor blind conservatism could, in the end, have affected the result. Sooner or later the opposition would have crumbled and, I believe, sooner rather than later,

In general, Shaw took a quiet, steady interest in people, events, and ideas. This observation of mine intrigued me and led me, less than a year after his death, to copy him. Shaw, in effect, taught me to live more outside myself. I had always read a lot, but my reading had been almost solely in the field of what could be called the classics – and for fun. Now I began to meddle in earnest inside the common media – newspapers, magazines, business weeklies, and borrowed news-letters. And I began to read ordinary biographies about ordinary people. Further, I began to talk and mix a little more. The changes came gradually; but they did come. And it was Shaw's influence that brought them about.

Shaw was always considerate and kind, even when working under difficulties. He was quietly friendly, but not warm. I came to feel that warmth had been physically and spiritually beaten out of him many years earlier on the rough, pitiless deserts of Arabia. His thoughtfulness for others was carried well beyond that standard shown by most of us during a working day; and it wasn't studied. He was never bad-tempered. He was generous, he would loan anything he owned without the slightest hesitation. He tipped well beyond his means and always repaid a kindness or service in some way or another. I found no fault in him, either as a mentor or as a workmate.

I have heard Shaw described as being enigmatic. He wasn't enigmatic, he was merely quiet. Everything he did that I knew about was understandable in his circumstances. I saw nothing puzzling in his idea of, for example, enlisting in the RAF and then remaining a lowly A/c2 throughout his service. I have known a number of outstandingly brilliant men who could well have taken a similar course in order to avoid irksome, often meaningless, responsibilities of one kind and another. Constantly to have to live up to an exalted reputation, or a long line of faultless performances, can grow extremely distasteful and painfully exhausting. Shaw, quite successfully I think, avoided these "wearing" predicaments.

I came completely under Shaw's spell. He was not like any other man I knew. There was nothing of the "I don't want to, and you shan't" attitude about him. He never begrudged me the independence he himself demanded; my opinions could always be expressed openly, without fear of being disregarded or, considering my *naïveté*, ridiculed.

I often had a feeling that many of my ideas and innovations in design that I put forward to Shaw were, in truth, his. I had noticed his habit of planting a seed in another's mind and his patient wait for its germination and flowering. It is reasonable to think that this kind of influence affected my thinking too. Such outside guidance is not easily discerned when oneself is the recipient.

Sometimes I would see Shaw leaning against an unmortared country wall, not far from my digs, his elbows resting on loose cap-stones, a poetry book in his hands. Such a picture made a quiet, peaceful scene; but I always got the feeling that action was only being suppressed, the coiled-up spring within him was ready for instant release at the first sign of the unexpected. His quiet reserve was impressive. This trait in his character, perhaps more than any other, has remained steadfastly in my memory over the years.

I think Shaw both liked and disliked being a legend and that this inner division embarrassed him, if not constantly, then much of the time. But at bottom and in general, he preferred to remain unknown and unnoticed. When caught off-guard and put on his mettle, he became the Lawrence we read about. I remember an incident in the yard: it was a case of unashamed negligence by a yard worker, when, in a quick aside to me, Shaw said, "I've shot men for less!" Shaw corrected the negligence (a blow-torch was being

160

operated far too close to a petrol pump) in a split second and without a "scene".

Our relationship was discreet, spasmodic and short-lived. It was discreet, because of necessity – he needed no yard gossip about our research work which might reach higher levels in the RAF or the daily newspapers. For my part, I had my job to guard in a touchy and jealous profession, inside a company that was hostile to the idea of any employee keeping even a privately discovered innovation to himself. The relationship was spasmodic because Shaw would be absent from the yard for days on end – sometimes for much longer. It was short-lived, because we met late in his life – I knew him for only nineteen months and of these only eleven were closely active.

I believe Shaw found our work purposeful and satisfying, free from tiresome, outside responsibility and burden. He seemed to enjoy our brainstorming sessions, with their flights of fancy, and the likely chances that some practical notions would separate from the fanciful and fall into our laps under the force of their own gravitational worth.

For me the relationship was one of great pleasure, pleasure in my being permitted to associate with a famous man, one who was an expert in the art and science of forecasting our country's defence needs. His brilliant intellect astounded and awed me. I think I realized that through him I was having bestowed on me a hearty and privileged kick up the backside into the future. The association did, in fact, alter and re-direct my life and work for the next six years; and I was to make use of the results we had obtained for the rest of my life. Further, through it all, I gained a pleasant research pastime that helped me to further our original work for another fifty years.

Shaw's humour never failed to surprise me. It was not the sophisticated humour of the scholar and the intellectual but, rather, that of the high-school practical joker. During my early days at Hythe, there was a story I heard which could have been true.

As I heard it, we had a yardman on our premises who had a flair for highly picturesque language. This fellow could continue his flowery tirades for long periods with perfect fluency and no repetition. Shaw, knowing this, slyly brought down from Felixstowe a longshoreman he knew who was also adept in this specialized and fanciful off-shoot of our language. Shaw, it was said, carefully plotted a confrontation between the two and, when this came about, he quietly stepped aside. A battle royal began. It raged with spirit and determination. Insults, thick and heavy, were flung with telling precision; the conflict was long, loud and hot. In the end, as Shaw had expected, our own champion ran dry of invectives. Hence, he was defeated, though not abjectly. Although he retired in disappointment, it was not in shame. To this day, I shudder and wilt when I recollect, as told to me, the opening broadsides of that doughty pair of warriors.

There were many social graces one had to forego when in Shaw's company. One did not help him on with his coat; invite him to join a small group for a chat; shake his hand; attempt close activity with a camera – however innocent the intent; or talk platitudes.

One excellent habit of Shaw's – I have remarked on it elsewhere – was his keenness to accept the advantages to be got from a new idea and to disregard, *pro tem*, any of its possible disadvantages. He would nurture a new thought along all its possible directions. Its disadvantages would be eliminated or reduced by further thought and rarely did a weak compromise have to be made. I was happy with such an attitude toward innovation, as would any practicing designer with a touch of originality in his soul; by it, I was willingly driven to give my best performances in his company.

In our talks we never clashed over our opinions. Poor ideas fell away naturally and the better ones found themselves high on our list for further investigation. Although carried out quietly and secretively, our talks were a pleasure and a hobby.

There are few people who realize the extraordinary depth and breadth of Shaw's perception in design. At its best it was, without exaggeration, remarkable. It showed itself clearly, often spontaneously, all the time we worked together; I often marvelled at this non-professional, yet professional-like ability. I learned quickly to take full advantage of this extra-sensory insight – for that is what it was – and it never failed me.

One day, because I had rather bitterly complained that water was a wet, messy, uncontrollable element, fit only for running over waterfalls and under bridges, he instinctively suggested using inwash fins – as we later called them – at each end of our boat's planing surfaces. His plan was to confine the water in its path under the boat, and so prevent it from shirking its job of providing lift for the hull. This was quick insight of high degree and I have often wondered if it were triggered by my word "uncontrollable".

As Dostoevsky wrote of the brother Alyosha in *The Brothers Karamazov*, so I have come to think of Shaw:

> "Here is perhaps the one man in the world whom you might leave alone without a penny, in the centre of an unknown city of a million inhabitants, and he would not come to harm, he would not die of cold and hunger, for he would find shelter for himself, and it would cost him no effort or humiliation. And to shelter him would be no burden, but, on the contrary, would probably be looked on as a pleasure."

Many men knew Shaw better and for longer than I did. In spite of the possible limitations on my judgement, I would like to venture my own carefully-considered guess that, after the intensive activity, frightful hardships and experiences of his youth, Shaw, in his later life, was bored, almost mortally bored. The uncertainties of peacetime and middle age were not for him and life, I sincerely believe, had become too simple, too slow and too dull. He missed the chase and the combat. Gone too were the excitement and hardship of life under an open sky, gone were the days of high purpose and idyllic self-sacrifice. The fire had departed his soul and the future loomed weak and colourless. I am certain he dreaded old age – "the shipwreck of old age", as General de Gaulle so truly and so courageously put it.

To most of us – those who knew him personally and those who knew him only by reading and hearsay – Lawrence of Arabia was the most famous, the most chivalrous and most heroic knight-errant since Sir Galahad, leader of the quest for the Holy Grail.

And, as Aircraftman Shaw, he was a good engineer too.

 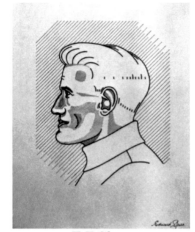

Edward Spurr   T E Shaw

(Spurr's own drawings)